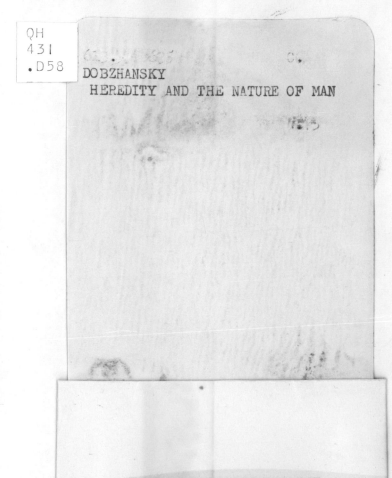

Heredity and the Nature of Man

Also by Theodosius Dobzhansky

GENETICS AND ORIGIN OF SPECIES

EVOLUTION, GENETICS, AND MAN

BIOLOGICAL BASIS OF HUMAN FREEDOM

MANKIND EVOLVING

HEREDITY AND THE
NATURE OF MAN

Theodosius Dobzhansky

Harcourt, Brace & World, Inc. / New York

To Alfred E. Mirsky

Preface

We live in the Age of Science. Considerably more than one half of the total number of scientists who ever lived are alive today. This seems to me one of the most startling statistics I ever came across. It means not only that there are more scientists now than there were in the past. The rate of growth of the number of scientists is more rapid than that of the number of people living on earth. The population of scientists is "exploding" more violently than is the population of mankind. The fraction of the world population now engaged in, and gaining its sustenance from, activities connected with science is greater than it was in the past, and it is rapidly increasing. Surely, this cannot continue indefinitely. The "population explosion" of mankind must stop before the food supply and the standing room on the surface of our planet are exhausted; the "explosion" of the population of scientists must stop before everybody becomes a professional scientist. But in our time science is growing faster than it ever has before, and probably faster than it ever will in the future.

This tremendous expansion of scientific activity is gratifying. It is, however, not quite an unmixed blessing. One may rejoice in seeing the prodigious rate of growth of the store of human knowledge taking place in one's lifetime. But the magnitude of this store has far outstripped the capacity of even the most powerful human intellects to assimilate all the knowledge. Irretrievably gone is the time when a scientist, and even simply an educated man, could be a person broadly familiar with the contemporaneous state of science as a whole. This is now not only impossible, but, for a working scientist, undesirable. The advancement of science is, in the main, the business of specialists. And as science expands, the specialists tend to become narrow specialists. Some specialists have become disgustingly narrow. Narrow specialists are endangered and dangerous—endangered because their own inner lives are impoverished; dangerous because they are liable to be easy prey for exploitation by those with power or with money, for purposes inimical both to science and to the interests of mankind as a whole.

Science is thus faced with a cruel paradox: it is its own growth that poses the gravest threat. Science risks being transformed into a kind of incommunicable mystery. Conceivably, it may even reach a stage when it will be no longer worth communicating. The remedy, if there is one, surely lies within science itself. The proliferation of specialties and specialists has never done away with the opposing tendency—generalization and synthesis. True enough, the more ponderous the corpus of scientific data dug up by the specialists becomes, the more difficult becomes the task of synthesis, and also the more obviously necessary. It should not be imagined that the specialists and the synthesizers are two different kinds of scientists. Specialists in synthesis are usually poor specialists and poor synthesizers. Ideally, every scientist ought to be a bit of both. This is too much to hope for, though; there is at least as much diversity of personality among scientists as among any other group of people. There should exist, however, scientists able and willing now and then to abandon the protective shells of their specialties, and to engage in surveying broader vistas. For scientists, this is often a dangerous occupation, since it is liable to imperil their standing as specialists. But like many other dangerous occupations, it is a necessary one in a modern society. People at large will have their inner life enriched if they gain an appreciation of what science and scientific attitude really are. Some aspects and some achievements of science are everyone's business.

The present book is based on the Holiday Science Lectures series, sponsored by the American Association for the Advancement of Science, and delivered in April 1963 at Los Angeles, California, and in March 1964 at Minneapolis, Minnesota. The purpose of the Holiday Science Lectures program is stated as follows: "to broaden the scientific horizons of the audience, and to communicate to them some of the excitement and inspiration of the scientific endeavor." This is certainly a difficult task for any lecturer to undertake, not least a geneticist. Among the many advances of science in our age, the development of genetics, the science of heredity, is one of the most impressive ones. To be sure, genetics has not invented a new kind of superbomb, nor can it match the romantic appeal of interplanetary travel. The interest and importance of genetics are in a different realm. More than two millennia ago, Greek sages discovered that to "Know thyself" is the foundation of all wisdom. Perhaps the chief aim and purpose, or at least one of the aims and purposes, of genetics, of biology, and even of science in general, is to help man to understand himself and his place in the universe.

In this book, no attempt will be made to survey the whole field of genetics. We shall be concerned mainly with the humanistic aspects of genetics, that is, with those basic facts, ideas, and conclusions most relevant to man, his origins, and his future.

The author wishes to acknowledge his obligation to the audiences who came to hear the Holiday Lectures and his other lectures for the many searching questions that were asked; these questions helped greatly to decide which topics needed greater elaboration and emphasis in this book. My colleagues, Professor A. E. Mirsky, Professor A. G. Bearn and Professor Bruce Voeller have read one of the draft manuscripts and offered their suggestions. Miss Patricia Hall has shown much patience and care in the preparation and typing of the manuscript. Chapters 2 and 3 are expanded versions of a lecture, variants of which were given at Vassar College, at Georgetown University, at Washington University, and at Yale University in 1963 and 1964. A condensed version of Chapter 3 has been published under the title "Genetics of Race Equality" in *Eugenics Quarterly,* vol. 10, no. 4, pp. 151-160, 1963. A part of Chapter 5 is taken from the article "Evolution—Organic and Superorganic," published in *The Rockefeller Institute Review* for 1963 and reprinted in the *Bulletin of the Atomic Scientists* for 1964.

THEODOSIUS DOBZHANSKY

The Rockefeller Institute, New York
August 1, 1964

Contents

Heredity and the Nature of Man

[I]

The Nature of Heredity

Ever since man became man, he has had to face the problem of how to live in a world together with other men. The problem grows more and more urgent as the number of people increases. According to the *United Nations Demographic Yearbook,* there were about 2,015,000,000 people in 1930. By 1950, mankind had expanded to 2,509,000,000, and by 1961, to 3,069,000,000. The annual growth rate of the world population between 1950 and 1961 was about 1.8 per cent. Inescapably, crowds become more prevalent than solitude. Nowadays, even a rugged and seemingly self-sufficient individualist will find it hard to withdraw from the throngs to live in seclusion in some desert, as ancient anchorites used to do. The pleasanter deserts tend to be utilized for winter resorts! More and more, man is forced to live up to the designation given him by Aristotle—*politikon zoon,* social animal, city animal, or "political" animal.

Humans are not only multitudinous; they are diverse. No matter how many people one meets, every person is different from all others. It is often hard to describe in words just what distinguishes Mr. X from Mr. Y, but the uniqueness of every person is so general an experience that it is taken pretty much for granted. Since 1823, when the anatomist J. E. Purkinje first showed that persons can be identified by their fingerprints, no authenticated case of indistinguishable finger patterns in different people has ever been found. Even so-called "identical" twins, about which more will be said below, are never really identical. They are, however, less different on the average than persons who are not twins, and this greater similarity strikes us as something extraordinary and remarkable.

Being humans, we perceive differences among humans more readily than differences among, say, sheep or flies. A shepherd may, however, recognize individually every sheep in a flock of hundreds, and a biologist can show that two identical flies are about as unlikely to be found as two identical humans. What makes people different from one another is a matter of no small importance, if we wish to understand our fellow human beings in order to live with them in reasonable harmony. Two ideas, neither of which ever lacked adherents, can be offered in explanation. One of them assumes that the diversity of humans is due to a diversity of their heredities, their natures. The other ascribes the differences between persons to the different environments, different nurtures. Both ideas have been stated in many forms, as political convictions, professions of faith, and scientific theories. Considered in the light of modern biology, both the hereditarian and the environmentalist theories are, as I hope to show in this book, equally unsound. The truth lies in between, or, rather, includes both the hereditarian and the environmentalist viewpoints. A person, any person, and all his physical, mental, and cultural characteristics, is a product of the interaction of nature and nurture, heredity and environment.

Ideas and theories may have very matter-of-fact and

practical consequences. The basic idea of environmental-ism was stated very clearly by John Locke in 1690; it achieved considerable popularity during the Age of Enlightenment, the eighteenth century; it greatly influenced Thomas Jefferson and some of his contemporaries; through them, it became one of the ingredients of the philosophy of democracy. According to Locke, a human being at birth is neither good nor bad. He is, rather, a *tabula rasa,* a clean slate, on which environment, upbringing, and education inscribe this or that collection of attributes and qualities. By means of good education, the good potentialities are introduced, conserved, and developed. The result will be a person with good habits, skills, and ideas, in short, a good citizen. Neither Locke nor Jefferson can be held responsible for the fact that their views have sometimes been stretched to mean that people ought to be made as much alike and uniform as possible. To many people, there is something wrong and "undemocratic" in giving a different kind of schooling and education to the more capable and to the less capable pupils. This is, of course, a perversion of democracy; it could only lead to a wastage of excellence in favor of mediocrity.

The hereditarian view is that man is a creature born with his character and abilities fixed and unchangeable. What he can and cannot accomplish in his life is essentially settled and predetermined by his heredity. The basic assumption was, in a way, stated by Aristotle, in his famous dictum "Those who are sprung from better ancestors are likely to be better men, for nobility is excellence of family." The history of the hereditarianism is, however, tortuous in the extreme. At least in Christian civilization, it may seem to find some support in the dogma of Adam's Original Sin. Inherited by all mankind, this sin makes human nature basically evil and depraved. The doctrine of predetermination, borrowed from St. Augustine and developed and elaborated by John Calvin and the Calvinist tradition, assumes that some humans are elect and others are damned by God's inscrutable decision. The decision is unalterable, but men and women show to which class they belong by the character of their lives. It would seem to be a long leap, which many people have nevertheless made with surprising ease, from this religious doctrine to the very secular view that a person's wealth and his position in society are also settled and predetermined by his heredity. It is God, or Nature, or heredity which has made some of us able and others inept, some clever and others stupid, some hard-working and others lazy.

Should one, then, make the world safe for the smart and the strong, and let the rest take care of themselves as best as they may? Or is it better to be guided by the lofty vision, which is the basis of the American tradition of democracy, that all men, though certainly different as individuals, have been created equal in the right to life, opportunity, and the pursuit of happiness? To hope that people will choose between such alternatives solely on the basis of biology or genetics would be more than a little naïve. Religion, ethics, historical traditions, emotions, and even passions will influence their choices. Scientific understanding is, however, at least one of the safest guides to follow.

By and large, persons resemble their parents more than they do unrelated individuals. This greater resemblance is due mostly to common heredity. A child has 50 per cent of his genes common with one parent, and 50 per cent with the other parent. It is to be expected that there will be a usually obvious correlation between parents and offspring in various traits. For example, I have a prominent nose, blue eyes, and my hair was blond; my parents had these characteristics also. However, I speak and write English, which, so far as I know, none of my ancestors did; my English is marred by a foreign accent of which most people with whom I speak are free. These differences came from environment.

Here a word of warning is necessary. One gets in trouble every time one tries to divide human traits into two neat categories, the hereditary and the environmental. Such a dichotomy is false and misleading. Most traits are influenced and modified by the heredity as well as by the environment. A simple example: My skin can be strongly tanned by outdoor life or bleached by living indoors. Yet nobody doubts that the skin pigmentation is influenced by heredity. Heredity is most often neither inexorable fate nor a "dice of destiny"; the reader of this book will time and again see evidence showing that heredity is, rather, a conditioning with which a new individual enters the world. What heredity does is set the stage for the interaction of the developing organism with its environment. The conditioning is, however, different in different persons. For example, some people (albinos) do not become tanned no matter how much sunlight they are exposed to, and others have dark skins even when they live indoors.

Sex Cells and Fertilization

Modern understanding of the nature of heredity is doubtless incomplete. Much remains to be learned. The present state of our knowledge is the outcome of at least three centuries of discoveries, made at ever-accelerating pace, by many scientists working in different countries. The gradual unfolding of the story of heredity is as fascinating as any other in the history of science. Apart from its intrinsic interest, even a brief review of the history of genetics should give a better appreciation of the subject than can be obtained in other ways.

It is curious that, although the fact of heredity is familiar to everybody from everyday observation, heredity is one of the most widely and persistently misunderstood phenomena of nature. The main source of the misunderstanding is an ambiguity of our language (and, it so happens, of most other languages). The words "heredity" and "inheritance" refer both to the biological inheritance and to the inheritance of property. Now, the statement that a person has inherited his skin color, or his facial features, or his intelligence from his parents means obviously something quite different from inheriting a house or a sum of money. Houses and money that the inheritor receives no longer belong to their former possessors. The parents do not, however, give away their skins or faces or brains when a child is conceived or born. A new individual arises from two minute parts of his parents' bodies—an egg cell and a spermatozoon (Figure 1). If "heredity" is taken to mean a

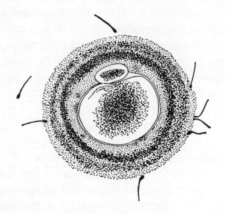

Figure 1. A human egg cell with several spermatozoa around it, one of which will enter the egg and stimulate it to develop. The polar body resulting from the first meiotic division can be seen above the egg cell proper.

transfer of material objects, then all that can be biologically inherited from one's parents are the sex cells with the genes the latter contain. "Inheriting" skin color or a musical talent becomes a metaphor—a statement meaning that the sex cells that gave rise to the inheritor contained something that gave him the potentiality of developing a certain skin pigmentation or an ability to appreciate, to play, or to compose music.

The fact that biological heredity is transmitted from

parents to offspring by means of the sex cells became known less than three centuries ago. This relative recency is not surprising; microscopes had to be invented before the existence of the sex cells could be suspected. As long as microscopes were not available, the seminal fluid was believed to be just that—mere fluid. We shall see in Chapter 2 that this confused a perspicacious early thinker about heredity—Montaigne—who could not understand how it was that he inherited from his father gallstones in the gall bladder, solid objects in a fluid.

Spermatozoa were discovered by Anthony van Leeuwenhoek (1632-1723). Leeuwenhoek is a figure who has always fascinated me. He was no professional scientist, but a rank amateur doing scientific research as a hobby. A prosperous merchant in the small town of Delft, Holland, he managed in his spare time to make several, in modern parlance, scientific "breakthroughs," which secured for him a place of honor in the history of science. In true "do-it-yourself" style, he occupied himself with grinding lenses and building microscopes. With the aid of these, he then examined all sorts of things in a rather haphazard and unsystematic fashion. A world of minute objects, which nobody had beheld before him, was revealed to his astonished eyes, and he described it in a charmingly naïve but straightforward fashion. The various kinds of "animalcules" that he found in stale water and in other materials were the infusoria and the bacteria of which he was the discoverer.

In 1677, Leeuwenhoek and his friend L. Hamm examined the seminal fluid of a man. They saw swimming in it minute bodies, the spermatozoa, and Leeuwenhoek sent an account of his discovery to the Royal Society of London. Here is a quaint detail: In an accompanying letter he begged the Society not to publish his findings if they thought these to be obscene or immoral. He then went on to say that he had obtained the objects to be examined not by what might be regarded a shameful or sinful method, but in what he believed a legitimate way. Fortunately, the

Royal Society agreed with Leeuwenhoek, and published his account of his discovery without delay.

That birds and some other animals lay eggs was, of course, common knowledge, but that similar structures exist in the ovaries of female mammals was discovered by Regneir de Graaf in 1673. Human egg cells were seen much later, by the German-Russian K. E. von Baer in 1827. Meanwhile, the Italian Lazzaro Spallanzani in 1785 had made brilliant experiments in artificial insemination. Just what part of the semen stimulates the egg cell to develop into a fetus and then into a child? Is it an exhalation, the odor, the *aura seminalis* of the seminal liquid, or is it one of the animalcules discovered by Leeuwenhoek? Frogs and toads are among the animals who procreate by external fertilization—both females and males discharge their sexual products in water, so the fertilization must take place outside the bodies of the parents. Spallanzani observed the "amours" of the frogs, collected the seminal fluid, filtered it to separate the liquid from the animalcules, and showed that the former no longer possessed the power to effect fertilization.

To show that what is true for the lowly frog is also true for animals much more like man, Spallanzani made similar experiments with dogs. He filtered the dog semen, and showed that the sperm-free filtrate did not cause pregnancy when injected in a bitch. The unfiltered sperm did. Spallanzani thus became the inventor of artificial insemination, and it is easy to understand his elation, expressed in the statement that this work gave him the greatest pleasure of his scientific life. Astonishingly enough, Spallanzani did not draw from his experiments the obvious conclusion: that the spermatozoa are the male generative elements. He was a partisan of the school of "ovists," who believed that it is only the egg that has the power to produce progeny; so, he supposed that the spermatozoa are needed only to enable the liquid part of the seminal fluid to stimulate the development. Even great scientists sometimes have their preconceptions!

Not until 1875 was fertilization itself, the union of an egg and a sperm, actually observed under a microscope; this was achieved by the German zoologist Oskar Hertwig. Sea urchins, like frogs, discharge egg cells and spermatozoa in water. The actively moving spermatozoa are attracted to the egg cells; a single spermatozoon then penetrates an egg cell, and the nuclei of the two cells fuse together. The fertilized egg then begins to cleave, to divide in two, four, eight, sixteen, and more cells, each cell receiving the entire sets of chromosomes that were present in the original egg cell and in the spermatozoon. Every cell of our bodies thus contains the products of the replication of the chromosomes derived both from the mother and from the father.

Chromosomes and Genes

In the nineteenth century, the character of biological science gradually changed. More and more, it became an occupation for professionals rather than for amateurs. Microscopes became better and better, but they also grew more expensive; biological research began to require well-equipped laboratories and libraries. Charles Darwin and Gregor Mendel, the two greatest figures of nineteenth-century biology, were nonprofessionals; the former was a well-to-do English country squire, the latter an Augustinian monk and the abbot of a monastery in Moravia. But, especially toward the end of the century, a biologist was usually a professional, and a professor at some university.

Genetics arose as a result of the confluence of two currents of discovery. The first was the study of cells, cytology. Peering through their microscopes, many cytologists gradually unraveled the cell structure and the processes of cell division, sex-cell formation, and fertilization. That cells are the units of which the bodies of organisms are composed was established by M. J. Schleiden and Theodor Schwann in 1839. Cell nuclei were seen by Robert Brown in 1831, but it was left to Eduard Strasburger (1875) and Otto Bütschli (1876) to show that nuclei arise by division of pre-existing nuclei through an amazingly complex but precise process called mitosis (Flemming, 1882). In the nuclei there are found bodies, chromosomes, which in dividing cells can be stained for easy visibility by certain dyes. These bodies have remarkable properties. The numbers and shapes of chromosomes tend to be constant in the body cells of each species of organism. Thus, nearly all of man's body cells carry forty-six chromosomes (the chromosome number in the human species was established, to be sure, much later, in fact, less than two decades ago). The sex cells, eggs and spermatozoa, contain half as many chromosomes as do body cells; human sex cells have twenty-three chromosomes. The formation of the sex cells involves a wonderfully complex but orderly process called meiosis, a series of chromosomal maneuvers reducing the chromosome number to one half of what it was in the primordial sex cells—forty-six to twenty-three in man (see Chapter 2 and Figures 7 and 8). The union of the male and female sex cells at fertilization restores the full number of the chromosomes in man from twenty-three to forty-six (P. J. van Beneden, 1883, and, especially, Theodor Boveri, 1887 and thereafter).

In the closing years of the nineteenth and the early years of the twentieth centuries, quite a number of cytologists (Boveri, Hertwig, Wilhelm Roux, Strasburger, August Weisman, E. B. Wilson, and others) suggested, more or less independently, that heredity is transmitted from parents to children chiefly, if not exclusively, through the chromosomes in the sex cells. From the vantage point of present knowledge, we know that these early pioneers were right. They reached the right conclusion by a process of brilliant inference, but on what we might now consider inadequate evidence. Their reasoning is quite interesting; it ran about as follows. A child may resemble his mother in some respects and his father in others, but on the average the contributions of both parents are about equal. And yet, eggs and spermatozoa are about as unlike in size and in appearance as two cells can be; in some animals an egg cell has a cytoplasmic mass millions of times greater than a spermatozoon. Indeed, the spermatozoon could be described as a nucleus provided with a tail, or flagellum, and very little cytoplasm. There is, however, one very prominent component that is similar in these two very different cells—the set of chromosomes they contain. The chromosomes are therefore fit to be the carriers of heredity. This sounds simple and obvious, but it took the efforts of several outstanding scientists to discover this "obvious" thing in the first place.

The second current of discovery started quite independently and inconspicuously with Gregor Mendel in 1865. As stated before, Mendel was not a professional scientist at all; he used his spare time to make experiments crossing different varieties of common kitchen peas. He kept careful records of the numbers of plants with different characters that appeared in the progenies of his crosses. His tremendous intellectual powers showed themselves in his analysis of these records, for he formulated the laws, or the rules, of heredity that are now called by his name. Nevertheless, his work was forgotten for more than thirty years, and was rediscovered, independently, by three different investigators in 1900.

How Mendel crossed his peas and how he counted the proportions among the hybrids of individuals with different traits and combinations of traits is described in any biology text. I shall not retell this story here. What follows from Mendel's experiments is, however, not always clearly stated, and yet the meaning of Mendel's work is as simple as it is important. The heredity transmitted in the sex cells is a collection of what Mendel called characters and we call genes, units that separate from one another and recombine in the process of sex-cell formation. One should realize clearly how great a departure the discovery of the genes made from the ideas generally accepted before this discovery, even by such outstanding scientists as Darwin (who never heard of Mendel or his work). Heredity was commonly believed to be transmitted by "blood"; this belief is reflected in our everyday language, in such expressions as "pure-blooded" and "half-blooded," which continue to be used even now. The parental "bloods" were assumed to mix in the child, so that the child's heredity was a blend, or a solution, of the heredities of his parents. After Mendel, we have to think of heredity not as a solution or an alloy of the heredities of the parents, but, rather, as a collection, or a mosaic, composed of discrete units, genes.

The next breakthrough in genetics was made possible by one of those insights that seem almost trivial after somebody explains them. Indeed, some of the most exciting moments in the life of a scientist come when he suddenly sees things that were before his eyes all the time; it is as though a blindfold falls from one's eyes. However that may be, in 1903, W. S. Sutton, in America, and, independently, Boveri, in Germany, saw that the behavior of genes discovered by Mendel is paralleled by that of chromosomes as seen under the microscope. In his work, Mendel probably never saw a chromosome; he inferred the existence of genes from the numerical ratios in which different types of offspring appeared in the progenies of the crosses he made. Genes have not been seen under a microscope even to this day. Sutton and Boveri had to make a mental leap from one field of study to what seemed to be a quite different field.

As stated before, the process of sex-cell formation involves the process of meiosis. Like other cells of the body, the cells from which the eggs and the spermatozoa develop contain two sets of similar chromosomes, one derived from the mother and the other from the father (see Figure 8).

During meiosis, the corresponding chromosomes of maternal and paternal origins come together in pairs. The cell now contains the same number of bivalents (chromosome pairs) as there were single chromosomes present in the sex cells. Next, each chromosome splits along its length, so that instead of pairs we now have groups of four chromosomal bodies (quadrivalents). The cell then divides twice without the chromosomes splitting again in the process, as they do during ordinary cell divisions. The result is that among the sex cells, the eggs and spermatozoa, that are formed, one half will carry the maternal (or, rather, grand-maternal) and the other half the paternal (now the grand-paternal) partner of the chromosome pair (Figure 8).

Let us now accompany Sutton and Boveri on their metaphorical leap from the chromosomes to Mendel's peas. Mendel had discovered that the genes do not blend, but segregate. If two varieties of peas that are crossed differ in that one variety has purple and the other white flowers, then both purple-flowered and white-flowered plants will be found among the hybrids in the second and later generations, and, at that, in predictable proportions. In the process of sex-cell formation in a hybrid, the genes of the purple and of the white parents separate cleanly and pass into different sex cells. They behave as if they were separate physical particles. A hypothesis can then be formulated: the chromosomes are the carriers of the genes.

Locating the Genes in the Chromosomes

A good scientific hypothesis is more than a guess, and even more than an ingenious guess. A good hypothesis is one that suggests experiments to be made, capable of either confirming the hypothesis or showing that it is wrong. The history of science shows that some hypotheses that were eventually rejected as wrong proved nevertheless useful, because they suggested and stimulated good experimental work. The hypothesis that chromosomes are the gene car-

riers proved not only fruitful, but also right. In the hands
of T. H. Morgan and his collaborators, working between
1910 and 1935, it became the foundation of a new branch
of knowledge sometimes called "cytogenetics." In each
living species the genes are divided into linkage groups; the
genes belonging to the same linkage group tend to be
inherited together; the number of the linkage groups was
found to be equal to that of the kinds of chromosomes.
Morgan correctly inferred that each linkage group is,
indeed, carried in a different chromosome. The genes
within a chromosome proved to be arranged in the chromosomes in a single linear file, like letters in a single line of
print on a page. Chromosomal "maps" were constructed
showing the arrangement of the genes in the chromosomes,
first in the vinegar fly (or pomace or fruit fly), *Drosophila
melanogaster,* and then in other genetically well-studied
organisms. Some very sketchy maps are now being constructed even for some of the human chromosomes.

The beauty of the work inspired by Morgan lies in its
predictive power. With Drosophila flies, experiments can
be planned and carried out crossing flies with different
characteristics, such as different colors of eyes, different
shapes of wings and bristles, and so on, and it can be pre-
dicted, both qualitatively and quantitatively, what will
be the distribution of these characteristics among the offspring. Usually the predictions are fulfilled, but on some
rare occasions they are not. Does the failure of a prediction
always show that the hypothesis on which the prediction
is based is wrong? Interestingly enough, such "failures"
happen sometimes to be the source of new discoveries.
This is the reason for the seemingly paradoxical aphorism
of the English geneticist William Bateson's "Treasure your
exceptions."

The following is an example of an eminently successful
application of this aphorism. Drosophila flies normally
have red eyes, but there are also strains with white eyes
(mutants). Morgan found, sometime in 1910, that crossing

white-eyed females with red-eyed males results in a progeny of red-eyed daughters and white-eyed sons (Figure 2). The reciprocal cross, red-eyed females to white-eyed males, gives a progeny of red-eyed flies of both sexes; the white eyes reappear only in the next generation (customarily designated the F_2 generation), in half of the sons but in none of the daughters (Figure 3).

To interpret the above results, Morgan used two hypotheses. First, the sex of a fly (and also of a human being) is determined by special chromosomes. A female has two so-called X-chromosomes, and all of her eggs contain an X-chromosome. A male has only one X-chromosome, and a chromosome not carried in females at all, called the Y-chromosome. The spermatozoa are consequently of two kinds—half of them carry the X-chromosome and the other half the Y-chromosome. An egg fertilized by an X-bearing sperm will have two X's, and will consequently develop into a daughter; the fertilization by a spermatozoon with the Y-chromosome gives a son, carrying one X- and one Y-chromosome. The second hypothesis is simply that the gene which permits the development of the red eye color, and its variant, which causes the eyes to be white (pigmentless), is carried in the X-chromosome. This gene is "sex-linked." To be sure, the first hypothesis, dealing with the chromosomal determination of sex, was put forward on the basis of numerous observations in addition to that of the inheritance of the red eye colors in Drosophila. The X- and Y-chromosomes can be seen under the microscope, and in Drosophila, they have distinguishable shapes.

The above rules of the inheritance of the red and the white eye colors in Drosophila flies are not without exceptions. The rules are usually "obeyed," but not always. Crossing white-eyed females to red-eyed males gives many thousands of red daughters and white sons, but there appear also an occasional white-eyed daughter or a red-eyed son. What has gone wrong? C. B. Bridges, a brilliant student of Morgan, undertook to analyze the rule more deeply

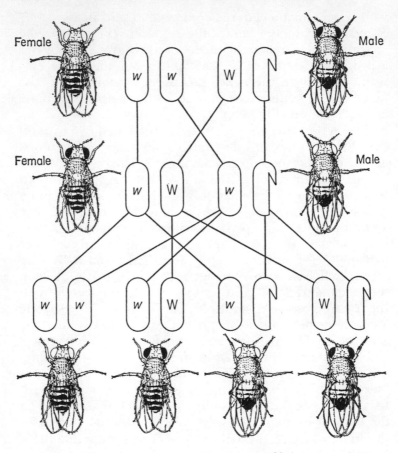

Females   Males

Figure 2. Inheritance of a trait, red vs. white color, the gene for which is carried in the sex chromosome of the fruit fly, *Drosophila melanogaster*. The progeny of a white-eyed female crossed to a red-eyed male.

by examination of the exceptions. Bridges reasoned as follows: The exceptional white-eyed daughters must have two X-chromosomes to be females, and they must obtain both these X-chromosomes from their mothers to be white-

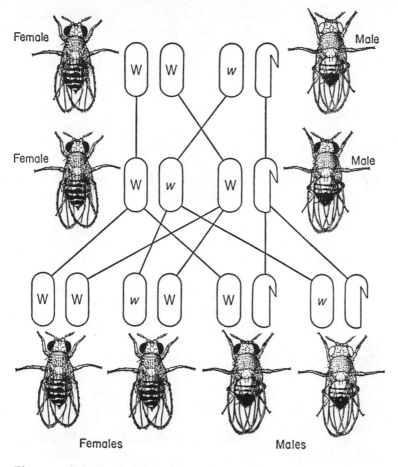

Figure 3. Inheritance of a trait, red vs. white color, the gene for which is carried in the sex chromosome of the fruit fly, *Drosophila melanogaster*. The progeny of a red-eyed female crossed to a white-eyed male.

eyed; the exceptional red-eyed sons must have a single X to be males, and they must receive their one X-chromosome from their fathers to be red-eyed. How can this be possible? Such results will arise if the meiosis in the egg cells is occasionally abnormal; the two X-chromosomes fail to disjoin and result in some exceptional eggs with two X's and some with none.

Here Bridges came to the critical point—how to submit his hypothesis to a rigorous test? To do so, he derived from the hypothesis a prediction. The exceptional white-eyed daughters must come from the exceptional eggs with two X-chromosomes fertilized by spermatozoa carrying Y-chromosomes. Consequently, these daughters must carry in their cells not only two X-chromosomes, but also a Y-chromosome. Such females were never seen before, yet the microscope settled the question; the prediction was correct. Another prediction was that the exceptional red-eyed sons must come from the eggs without X-chromosomes fertilized by X-bearing spermatozoa; they must have in their cells a single X-chromosome and no Y-chromosome. This prediction was also verified by microsopic examination. (Two further predictions can also be made. The eggs with two X-chromosomes fertilized by X-bearing spermatozoa must give individuals with three X-chromosomes. These individuals are the so-called "superfemales"; they are poorly viable, but they were eventually discovered by Bridges. The eggs with no X-chromosomes fertilized by Y-bearing spermatozoa die at an early stage of development, but they also were discovered and studied, by D. F. Poulson).

Feats of prediction and successful verification have been achieved again and again. When unusual results are observed in crosses of strains of Drosophila flies, one can ordinarily infer that these flies have some specific abnormalities in their chromosomes. Chromosomal abnormalities can be seen under the microscope. And, conversely, if one knows that a fly has some chromosomal abnormality, one can predict the results to be obtained if this fly is used as a parent in certain crosses. An experienced geneticist can "play" with the genes and the chromosomes of Drosophila flies almost like a chess player with his chess figures.

Chromosome Chemistry

The work of the Morgan school on Drosophila genetics and cytogenetics attained such a degree of refinement that after it the next development in the understanding of the physical basis of heredity could only come, and it did come, from the study of the chemistry of chromosomes. The two classes of chemical compounds that account for most of the material composing a chromosome are deoxyribonucleic acids (abbreviated as DNA) and proteins, loosely joined to form nucleoproteins. The question naturally arises, what makes one gene different from another? A human sex cell contains probably no fewer than 10,000 different genes, and there may be millions and millions of kinds of genes in different organisms in the living world.

Until fairly recently, say twenty years ago, most biologists were inclined to regard the proteins as probably responsible for the specific qualities of each gene. At present, it is considered extremely probable that heredity, genetic information, to use a now-fashionable phrase, is stored chiefly in the chromosomal DNA. Let us see what has led to this change of opinion. The nucleic acids are seemingly rather too simple and too uniform in chemical composition in most diverse organisms to produce a variety of structures at least equal to the variety of genes that exist in the living world. Proteins are, on the contrary, large, some of them being enormous, molecules; they exist in a great variety of forms, and they can be envisaged to produce almost infinite variety.

Facts began, however, to come to light that argued for the nucleic acids being the chief carriers of genetic information. A. E. Mirsky in the United States, R. Vendrely in France, and others found that the amount of DNA per cell doubles in the interval between successive cell divisions, and is reduced by half when the cell divides. However, this amount is remarkably constant in body cells of a given species of organism, except that the sex cells contain only half as much DNA and half as many chromosomes as do body cells. The chromosomal proteins are, on the contrary, quite variable, both in amount and in composition in different cells of the same body.

O. T. Avery, C. M. MacLeod, and M. McCarty discovered in 1944 that hereditary characteristics can be transferred from one strain of bacteria to other strains, causing pneumonia (*Pneumococcus*) by means of a transforming principle extracted from the donor strain. This "transforming principle" was identified as a nucleic acid. Such transformations of the hereditary endowment are now known in several species of bacteria; whether this is also possible in higher organisms remains to be seen. A. D. Hershey secured a very elegant demonstration of the importance of DNA in the transmission of heredity in his study of the bacteriophages (bacterial viruses). A bacteriophage is an organism too small to be seen in an ordinary light microscope but visible in electron microscopes; it enters living bacterial cells, multiplies therein, and causes the bacteria to disintegrate, releasing numerous new bacteriophages. Now, the body of a bacteriophage consists of a DNA core and a protein envelope; Hershey showed that only the DNA enters the host bacterial cell, while the protein is left outside.

The amounts of the DNA involved in the transmission of heredity are actually remarkably small, even in higher organisms. For example, the nucleus of the spermatozoon of a fish (carp) contains about 1.6 billionths of a milligram (1.6×10^{-12} of a gram) of DNA, while the nuclei of the body cells (red blood cells) contain 3.0 to 3.3 billionths. (This variation is probably a matter of imprecision in measurement.) Another fish (trout) has 2.45 of the same units of DNA in a spermatozoon, and 4.9 in a body-cell nucleus. Spermatozoa of a bull have 3.3 units, body cells some 6.4 to 6.8. Human body cells contain 6.0 to 6.8 units; the amount in human sex cells does not seem to have been measured.

One can make an interesting calculation of the total amount of DNA that has contained and has transmitted the genetic endowment of mankind. Take three billion (3×10^9) as the number of human beings now living; each of them arose from a fertilized egg cell, the nucleus of which had between 6 and 7×10^{-12} gram of DNA; all these egg cells had, then, between 0.018 and 0.021 of a gram, roughly 20 milligrams of DNA. Truly, the powers concealed in this extraordinary substance exceed by far anything in the atomic and other bombs yet invented!

Lower organisms generally have less DNA than higher ones. Thus, a bacteriophage (bacterial virus) has only 0.0002×10^{-12} of a gram; a colon bacterium (*Escherichia coli*), 0.01; the nucleus of a cell of a sponge, 0.1; of a sea urchin, 1.97; of a mouse, 5; of a man, as stated above, between 6 and 7. Man is, however, far from the top of the series. More DNA than in human cells is contained in a cell nucleus of the amphibians, such as a toad (7.3), a frog (15.0), *Necturus* (48), and *Amphiuma* (168). The meaning of this is obscure—in our pride we would not like to entertain the notion that toads, frogs, and salamanders need either more numerous or more complicated genes than man does. One possible but unconfirmed explanation might be that in some organisms the chromosomes of the cell nuclei contain the set of genes each represented only once, while in other organisms each gene of the set is repeated several times.

The chemical structure of DNA is a fascinating story in its own right. Many outstanding investigators in different parts of the world have been working on it in recent years, and with outstanding success. The results obtained are of the greatest importance; so much so, that it seems in the highest degree likely that our time will stand, in the history of biology, as that of the discovery of the chemical basis of heredity. Furthermore, it is sometimes said that truly great discoveries in science are beautifully simple; I am not sure that this proposition can always be sustained, but it certainly applies to the DNA story. Its essentials can be stated briefly and simply, without going into chemical details. DNA (Figures 4 and 5) extracted from the chromosomes of cell nuclei can be broken down to a fairly small number of constituents. These are a kind of sugar called deoxyribose, a phosphoric acid, and four so-called nucleotide bases, namely adenine, guanine, cytosine, and thymine. We shall not discuss the chemical structure and chemical formulae

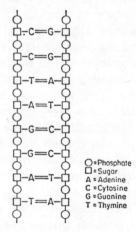

Figure 4. The composition of the DNA (deoxyribonucleic acid), the substance which carries the master blueprints of heredity in the form of a genetic "code." Two chains of sugars and phosphates are cross-linked by pairs of nucleotide bases, C-G or A-T.

of these constituents; furthermore, we shall take the liberty of denoting the adenine, guanine, cytosine, and thymine nucleotide bases simply by their initial letters, A, G, C, and T. Only rarely, in some exceptional organisms, is one of the bases replaced by a closely related chemical compound. This uniformity is, of course, in itself a most remarkable fact, attesting the fundamental unity of all that lives.

The DNA obtained from a series of quite diverse organisms has been submitted to chemical analysis. A suggestive regularity has emerged: namely, the content of A always equals, within limits of analytical error, that of T, and the content of G is the same as C. By contrast, the amount of A + T in relation to that of G + C is variable, some organisms being relatively richer in A + T and others in G + C (Table 1). This suggests that in the intact DNA, as it exists in the chromosomes, every A component is somehow paired with a T, and a G is paired with a C.

Two biochemists, J. D. Watson, in the United States, and F. H. C. Crick, in England, derived from these data a brilliant hypothesis. They envisaged how the component parts are put together to give a DNA molecule. Their

TABLE 1

The relative amounts of the nucleotide bases adenine (A), cytosine (C), guanine (G), and thymine (T) in the deoxyribonucleic acids (DNA) extracted from different organisms

ORGANISM	A : T	G : C	(A + T) : (G + C)
BACTERIOPHAGE	1.00	1.09	1.87
COLON BACTERIA	1.09	0.99	1.00
YEAST	0.96	1.08	1.80
SEA URCHIN	1.02	1.01	1.85
SALMON	1.02	1.01	1.43
CATTLE	0.99	1.00	1.37
MAN	1.00	1.00	1.54

celebrated model of the DNA structure shows something like a rope ladder wound up in a spiral (represented in Figures 4 and 5). The vertical part of the "ladder" is a monotonous sequence of the deoxyribose sugars and phosphates. The "rungs" of the "ladder" consist of the A, G, C, and T residues; there are two kinds of "rungs"—in one

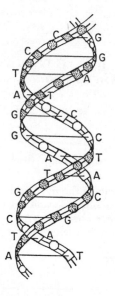

Figure 5. A representation of the Watson-Crick model of the structure of the DNA (deoxyribonucleic acid). The two cross-linked chains shown in Figure 4 are wound in a double helical spiral.

of them, A is coupled with T; in the other kind, G is coupled with C. Here, then, is an explanation of the fact that the DNA's obtained from most diverse organisms contain as many A's as T's and as many C's as G's, so that the ratios of their amount are always close to unity; the members of these pairs are the necessary complements of each other.

The Watson-Crick model provides a solution to the problem mentioned above, namely, how can there be so many kinds of genes if all of them have their distinctive properties specified by their DNA? This solution is best explained by means of an analogy. There are some 400,000 words in the English language, yet all these words can be spelled with only twenty-six letters of the alphabet. In fact, all of them can also be spelled with only three "letters"—in the Morse telegraphic code's dot, dash, and gap. A line in a printed page consists of words; words contain different letters, or the same letters differently arranged. The genetic "alphabet" consists of the four "letters" A, T, G, C; different combinations of them can give a virtually infinite variety of genetic "words" or "messages." The matter may also be looked at in another light—in the light of evolution. The evolutionary development of the living world has evidently taken place on the levels of the genetic words and messages, while the genetic alphabet has remained virtually unaltered throughout. Man differs from a Drosophila fly, a corn plant, or a bacteriophage by virtue of the fact that his gene endowment contains different messages, but these messages are conveyed by means of the same alphabet.

The genes are, then, sections of the DNA ladder-like molecules; different genes are different because they contain different sequences of the "letters" A, T, G, and C. It can be said that heredity is "coded" in the genes, or in the DNA of the chromosomes, in a manner similar to a message written in Morse code or in some secret code used by diplomats, generals, or spies. The day may not be far away when the sequences of the genetic "letters" in the various genes in man and in other organisms may become known. It is, however, a tremendous achievement to have understood the method of construction of the genetic messages, even if, for the time being, we cannot spell many of them out ourselves in the laboratory.

How Genes Make Their Own Copies

The Watson-Crick model has suggested a solution for another knotty biological problem. When a cell divides, its chromosomes split in equal halves, so that the daughter cells receive the same chromosomes, and presumably the same genes, the mother cell had. To say that a gene "splits" suggests, however, a crude and inaccurate picture of what actually happens. What a gene in fact appears to do is to manufacture its own copy, another gene just like itself. The self-copying, or replication, of the genes has to be very precise and accurate if the heredity is to be maintained and the progeny is to resemble the parents. Let us, then, represent a portion of the DNA "ladder" lying horizontally, like this:

Now suppose that the "rungs" of the "ladder" break, and that each C attracts to itself a G and vice versa, and that each A attracts a T and vice versa. The result would then be two "ladders" similar to each other and to the original one. (The capital letters stand for the original components and the small ones for the new components.)

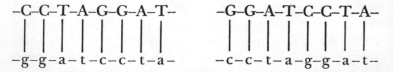

An individual receives, then, his heredity in the form of the two genetic "messages" encoded in the DNA of the two sex cells, the egg cell from the mother and the spermatozoon from the father. These two cells unite at fertilization, and initiate the long and complex series of processes in the development of the individual. The fertilized egg is a single cell; it divides in two, four, eight, and finally billions of cells; the cells form an embryo, then a fetus, an infant, a child, an adolescent, an adult, an oldster. An individual develops as long as he lives. Growth and maturation, as well as senescence and old-age decrepitude, are parts of the sequence of the developmental process. Looked at from the standpoint of genetics, the development of an individual may be said to represent a translation, or a decoding, of the genetic messages this individual received from his parents. Little is known at present, and much is to be learned, about the precise ways in which this translation of the genetic messages really takes place in the growing and developing organism when its organs are formed and its cells differentiate. The physiology of the development is a field of study rapidly developing at present.

Genes and Proteins

Some of the most important constituents of all living bodies belong to the class of chemical compounds known as proteins. The hemoglobin of red blood cells, the myosin of the muscles, the pepsin and trypsin so essential for the digestion of food, and numerous enzymes indispensable to the life of body cells, all are proteins. The human body contains no fewer than 10,000 and possibly as many as 100,-000 different kinds of proteins. Mention has already been made that proteins are large, some of them enormous, chemical molecules. Chemists discovered, however, that under the influence of acids or alkalis, proteins can be broken up into much smaller constituents. These constituents are amino acids. There is no need to describe here the chemical structure of the amino acids. What is important for us is that there are about twenty different kinds of amino acids which are the constituents of most known proteins. The proteins consist of long chains of amino-acid residues; these chains may be linked together by cross-connections, and may be coiled in various complicated but specific ways. Protein molecules may be long and slender fibers, or more or less spherical or globular in shape. Different proteins contain different sets and proportions of the twenty known amino acids. Moreover, the properties of a protein depend upon the exact alignment of the amino-acid residues in the chains.

One may say that the protein "alphabet" consists of about twenty "letters," the different amino acids. By analogy with the DNA nucleic acids, with their four genetic "letters," one may attempt to represent the structure of the proteins in terms of the twenty amino-acid "letters." The difficulty here is that, as indicated, a protein molecule may contain several different amino-acid chains with various cross-links and convolutions. In other words, the "letters" in a protein are not necessarily all disposed in a single line; they may form a complicated three-dimensional structure consisting of several amino-acid chains. The analogy with DNA is nevertheless a useful one, because the chief function the genes play in the development is to direct the synthesis of the proteins. Some authorities consider it probable that every gene specifies the sequence of the amino acids in just one chain composing a certain enzyme or some other protein the body must contain. To put it differently, the genetic message encoded in the DNA of the gene in the form of the sequence of the letters A, T, G, C is translated into the sequence of the amino-acid "letters" in a chain composing a certain protein.

In recent years, biochemists have obtained some very valuable information concerning the ways and means whereby this "translation" of the DNA four-letter code into the twenty-letter amino-acid code is actually accomplished (Figure 6). It appears that the "translators" are still-different substances, the ribonucleic acids, abbreviated RNA. RNA differs from DNA in several respects. It contains a different kind of sugar, a ribose instead of deoxyribose. It is at least usually single-stranded, instead of double-stranded with "rungs" like a ladder. It contains the base called uracil instead of thymine. The four-letter alphabet of RNA thus differs in one letter from DNA—it is A, U, G, C, instead of A, T, G, C.

The process of translation of the DNA message into the amino-acids sequence in the protein happens in the following way (Figure 6). First, a strand of RNA is formed, in which the sequence of the "letters" in a section of the DNA strand is impressed in a corresponding sequence of the RNA. The result is called the messenger RNA. It comes out from the cell nucleus into the cell cytoplasm, and attaches itself to the surface of very tiny bodies called ribosomes, visible only with the aid of electron microscopes. A series of amino acids then becomes arranged in a chain characteristic of a given protein and corresponding to the sequence of the "letters" in a given messenger RNA. Each amino acid in the protein is specified by a sequence of three "letters" in the RNA and the DNA. Successful attempts have been made in recent years to break this "triplet code," that is, to determine just which groups of three "letters" in RNA and DNA correspond to each one of the twenty amino acids. So spectacularly rapid has been the progress in this line of endeavor that the code is now well on the way to being deciphered, although some problems still await solution. One, perhaps rather unexpected, feature is that the code proved to be a degenerate one. "Degeneracy" (the word here does not imply that the code was in the past somehow better or more efficient than it is now) means that instead of a strict one-to-one correspondence between an RNA triplet and an amino acid, some amino acids can be specified by two or more different triplets.

Origin of Life

The foregoing pages have attempted to outline, of necessity in a very condensed and even superficial manner, the remarkable progress the study of heredity has made since

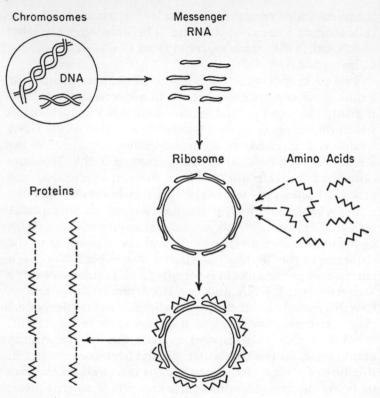

Figure 6. A schematic representation of how the genes act to build proteins, some of which act as enzymes. The DNA of the genes in the chromosomes impresses its specificity on another substance, the messenger RNA. This "messenger" passes from the cell nucleus to the cytoplasm, and settles on the surface of very minute bodies called ribosomes. Amino acids then become linked together in orders specified by the messenger RNA, to form different proteins.

the pioneer microscopists first sighted the sex cells. The remainder of the present chapter will deal with a frankly speculative matter: the origin of life on earth. Man has discovered that he is a product of evolution of living matter, and he cannot refrain from asking whence he, together with everything that lives, ultimately came.

The development of ideas about the origin of life went through at least three phases. To those unfamiliar with biology, the problem appeared to be very simple, or, rather, the problem did not seem to exist at all. Primitive man was an animist, believing that all natural objects possess some sort of life or vitality. He was ready to assume that living beings arise from nonliving materials all the time. Countless legends and myths relate, often with great poetic elegance, how diverse animals and even men appeared out of stones, earth, or simply from the air. More prosaically, it was generally credited that fly maggots arise from putrid meat, lice from dirty clothing, and mice from old rags. As a cheeky youth, I remember having angered a dear old lady by refusing to believe that clothes moths will appear in the stored woolens if no moth comes in from the outside. She did not know, or care to know, that Francesco Redi and Spallanzani had already proved, in the seventeenth and eighteenth centuries, that spontaneous generation of life does not occur—an example, I suppose, of what is politely called the "academic lag."

After Louis Pasteur's classical work of 1862, the principle *omne vivum ex vivo* (all life arises from life) became the fundamental tenet of biology. Darwin's theory of evolution, of "descent with modification," was taken to explain the development of the living world, from the lowest to the highest forms, from "amoeba to man," as it used to be formulated. This theory did not, however, pretend to explain how the lowest organisms arose in the first place. Biological evolution was supposed to start with an "amoeba"; nowadays, we prefer to start with some primordial virus, since the amoeba is much too complicated an organism already. The Swedish astronomer S. A. Arrhenius in 1907 proposed an escape: Life is present in many parts of the universe, and its seeds were introduced on our planet with some sort of cosmic dust. Nobody has ever found any such seeds coming in from cosmic space. This is not the only flaw in Arrhenius' hypothesis. The problem is merely pushed back in time, and the question immediately arises: How did life start in the cosmos?

The spectacular recent advances of biochemistry and genetics have imbued biologists with enough self-confidence to face again the problem that for so long seemed beyond reach, namely, creating life in the laboratory from nonliving constituents. Such a feat is yet to be achieved. It is, however, interesting to consider briefly some experiments that come nearest, to date, to this achievement. A. Kornberg (now at Stanford University) prepared a mixture of the component parts of DNA, that is, of the "letters" A, T, C, and G. His preparation actually contained them in the form of deoxynucleoside triphosphates of adenine, thymine, cytosine, and guanine. The problem was, of course, how to link these components together as they are linked in the DNA.

Kornberg extracted from the colon bacterium an enzyme that can mediate the reaction of linking. The addition of the enzyme to the mixture of the triphosphates of A, T, C, and G did not, however, suffice to accomplish the synthesis of DNA. What was missing was a "primer." Kornberg, in 1956, found that a small amount of DNA extracted from some living organism could serve as such a primer. The addition of a primer caused the appearance in the preparation of DNA molecules. Most important of all, the DNA synthesized was identical in the proportions of the different nucleotides (the "letters") not to the DNA of the organism furnishing the enzyme, in this case the colon bacterium, but to that furnishing the primer. Kornberg was able to induce the synthesis of the DNA characteristic of a bacteriophage, of at least two species of bacteria, and of cattle by using as primers DNA extracted from these organisms.

In Kornberg's experiments, the molecules of the primer DNA "reproduced" themselves. Or, to be more precise, they served as models, or templates, for the synthesis of their copies. The genes in the chromosomes of living cells reproduce themselves probably by means of a priming mechanism of the same kind that operated in Kornberg's experiments. One would, of course, like to see an experiment performed with a synthetic primer, instead of with a primer taken from a living cell. Is this a possible goal? In a recently published work, Kornberg and his colleagues L. L. Bertsch, J. F. Jackson, and H. G. Khorana seem to be well on the way to this achievement. When it is finally achieved, one will have to face a tough question: Does this mean that life has been created artificially? It must at the very least be admitted that this would give us a good model of life, even though it may not re-create a facsimile of any actually existing life.

At the base of it all there is, just the same, a real problem: What was the origin on earth, or anywhere in the universe, of the first "primer," which initiated the process of self-copying, the fundamental characteristic of life. For the time being this remains an unsolved riddle. But the problem is a meaningful one, and it is within this larger context that many biologists, chemists, astronomers, and geologists have been doing some interesting experiments, and a great deal of speculative writing. The results obtained by A. I. Oparin, in Russia, J. D. Bernal, in England, and Harold Urey, Stanley Miller, M. Calvin, S. W. Fox, and Harlow Shapley, in the United States, are in general agreement on one basic point: the primeval conditions on earth, which existed before there was any life, permitted the formation of certain chemical compounds that are now formed, exclusively or at least principally, in living bodies.

The atmosphere of the young planet Earth was very different from the one we breathe; it had little or no free oxygen, but it did contain, in addition to water vapor, the hydrocarbon methane (CH_3) and ammonia (NH_3). The chemical reactions that could take place in such an atmosphere have been explored by Stanley Miller and others. In

Miller's classical experiment of 1953, at least two amino acids, alanine and glutamic acid, were obtained in a vessel containing water, hydrogen, methane, and ammonia under the influence of electric discharges. There is now good evidence that a number of organic compounds, formaldehyde, acetic and several other organic acids, as well as five amino acids, can be formed in a mixture of gases resembling the atmosphere of the primordial earth under the influence of high-energy ultraviolet radiations, electric discharges, and perhaps other agencies. The waters of the seas and oceans were probably a kind of thin "soup," a dilute solution of some of the substances now formed in living organisms. Larger and more complex organic molecules, particularly proteins and nucleic acids, could conceivably arise in such a "soup," although this has not yet been conclusively demonstrated experimentally under realistically contrived "primitive" conditions. Oparin believes that an important process was the formation of so-called coacervate droplets, simple colloidal suspensions; Bernal thinks that protein molecules may have been formed owing to absorption of amino acids on the surface of clay particles.

All this adds up to the surmise that the first life could have arisen under the conditions that once existed on earth. The critical step, the appearance of the first self-replicating molecule or a combination of molecules, still seems, however, to be an improbable event. As long as this step is not reproduced experimentally, there will exist a difference of opinion about how it occurred. Some scientists are so headstrong as to believe that the surmise is plausible enough to be accepted as a probable description of what happened in reality. Given eons of time—and our planet is known to be at least three billion years old—a highly improbable event can take place somewhere, or even in several places, in the universe. Perhaps the first spark that kindled the flame of life did occur on earth, this insignificant little speck in vast cosmic spaces. Shapley seems to be convinced that life *must* exist also on some other planets, in many solar systems, and in galaxies other than our own. On the other hand, some people continue to regard the origin of life not only as an unsolved but also as an unsolvable mystery. They are as firmly convinced as ever that an act of God must have been invoked to contribute that first spark. I strongly feel that this point of view must not be ignored but must be faced honestly in a book dealing with the humanistic aspects of biology, even though it is impossible to attempt here more than an indication of the broad lines of the relevant arguments.

That there occur in living bodies many chemical and physical processes similar in principle to those observable in inert bodies is not doubted by anyone. Thus, nutrition is analogous to stoking an engine with fuel, and respiration to the combustion of that fuel. The question is whether *in addition* to such processes there are also in life other processes, forces, or agents which are not composed of physicochemical ones. Mechanists hold that such additional, irreducible, specifically vital forces do not exist. Vitalists believe that they do, and call them by a variety of names—the vital force, entelechy, psyche. Vitalism is at present a minority opinion, but it is a minority not because the mechanists have actually "explained" every one and all biological phenomena by reducing them to physics and chemistry. It will be argued in the next chapter that reductionist explanations are not always the most meaningful ones. Mechanists have achieved something perhaps better than a simple reduction. The living world is, hopefully, understandable as the outcome of the formation of progressively more and more complex and perfect compounds or patterns of physico-chemical processes in the course of biological evolution.

Biologists have rejected vitalism not because it has been proved that in no biological phenomenon may there be lurking a vital force. One cannot prove a universal negative. It is, rather, that vitalism has been shown to be unnecessary. Actually, the best argument that a vitalist can offer is that a mechanistic universe is too dull, flat, and uninteresting. Most vitalists are also theists. They are looking for gaps left between scientifically understandable events, hoping to have these gaps filled with God's interventions. The origin of life is one such gap. There are certainly innumerable others. They become, however, inexorably fewer and fewer as science progresses. Therefore, a supernatural God becomes less and less necessary. I am convinced that religion in the Age of Science cannot be sustained by the assumption of miraculous events abrogating the order of Nature. It should, rather, see acts of God in events the natural causes of which it fully understands. Then and only then nature as a whole, organic and inorganic, human and prehuman, macrocosmic and microcosmic, becomes a field for God's eternal and continuing, immanent and transcendent, natural and providential activity.

To those who ascribe the origin of life to God's special intervention it can be pointed out that this makes God simply another physico-chemical agent, but one perversely concealed from observation because it acts so very rarely. Suppose that it was God who some two billion years ago compounded the four kinds of nucleotides into the first DNA strand capable of self-replication. Was God then an enzyme of a peculiarly complex structure which no chemist can synthesize? But what if some bright chemist in the future synthesizes this enzyme, or at least figures out what chemical structure it must have had? And this predicament is not peculiar to the problem of the origin of life—it occurs every time one chooses to invoke God's intervention into natural processes. Does it make sense, for example, to think that organic evolution is guided by God's intervention? This would presumably mean that God induces from time to time some unusual mutations of a special kind, or that He directs the chromosomes to form particular gene combinations. There is certainly no compelling reason to make such assumptions. The origin of life and the emergence of human self-awareness were the crucial events of the evolutionary development of the cosmos. They certainly did take place here, on earth; we do not know whether similar events happened elsewhere in the universe. Be that as it may, creation is a process, not an act; it was not completed some five thousand or any other number of years ago; it continues now, before our eyes, and is accessible to scientific study.

[II]

Variety of Human Natures

Montaigne, an astute and quick-witted thinker of the French Renaissance, wrote, about four hundred years ago, that, in his opinion, heredity is an unfathomable mystery of Nature. His arguments continue to be interesting today. Montaigne believed that he had inherited from his father a painful ailment—gallstones in the gall bladder. However, his father first began to suffer from gallstones twenty-five years after his son was born, so, asks Montaigne, how could the father transmit to his son something that he did not have when the son was conceived? Montaigne himself was forty-five years old when he first felt the presence of gallstones; where was his inheritance hidden for so long a time? And anyway, how can stones be transmitted in the semen, which in Montaigne's time was believed to be mere liquid? Darwin made a painstaking collection of data on heredity available in his time, almost three centuries after Montaigne; he wrote that "The whole subject of inheritance is wonderful," but he realized quite clearly that it continued to be puzzling in many ways.

The growth of genetics since Darwin and Mendel, and especially since the rediscovery of Mendel's work in 1900, has made heredity no longer so mysterious. Montaigne's difficulty was in part that he did not realize the profound difference between biological heredity on the one side and the inheritance of property on the other (see page 7). Surely, he did not inherit gallstones from his father; he inherited his father's genes, which had been present in his father during the latter's whole life, and which in certain environments predisposed the father's and the son's organisms to develop gallstones. The inheritance of many traits, including many human traits, is at present fairly well known and, under certain conditions, predictable. The biochemical studies on the constituents of the chromosomes, very briefly reviewed in the first chapter, have given an at least plausible, and probably also essentially correct, picture of how heredity really works on the molecular level.

These splendid achievements of genetics are, however, only an auspicious beginning of man's quest for an understanding of the living world and, most significant of all, for an understanding of human nature. How does this remarkable substance DNA, with its "four-letter" genetic "alphabet," work on the level of the whole organism? How did it manage to evolve the countless different living beings, from a microbe to a sequoia tree and from an amoeba to man? Why are the structures and functions of the bodies of most of these creatures so wonderfully adapted to the ways of living and to the environments in which these creatures occur? And why, despite this universal adaptableness, do hereditary diseases, malformations, and weaknesses of various sorts afflict some individual humans and animals and plants? To what extent are the differences between persons and populations due to their genes and to their environments? Can genetic differences be overcome by environmental engineering? Man is a product of an evolutionary development that is still going on; is this evolution taking mankind in a direction that we, as humans, consider good and desirable? Can and should man take the management of his evolution in his hands, and, if so, what goals should be striven for and how can they be attained?

The reader should be warned at the outset: there are no complete, well-established, and generally agreed-upon answers to any of these questions. These questions should serve more as a program for further research than as a summary of past achievements. To me at least, the fact that there is so much in science that is yet unknown, but knowable, is even more inspiring than contemplation of the imposing store of the knowledge already gathered.

Individuality

H. L. Mencken, the amiably skeptical wit and cheerful pessimist of a generation ago, was sure that "human nature doesn't change." This was, to be sure, one of the least original of his ideas; almost everybody feels that life has taught him something about this thing called "human nature," and that it is some kind of a constant which must be reckoned with but not tampered with. Strangely enough, those who talk and write most glibly about human nature rarely consider what should be the first question about it: Is there one human nature or many different human natures?

The "divine" Plato, the greatest philosopher of antiquity, thought that what we observe in the world around us are mere shadows, reflections of the eternal and immutable ideas or archetypes which exist in the heavens or in some invisible world. People whom we meet are, then, only more or less defective and distorted images of the one ideal, perfect, and inconceivably beautiful man. Plato was not a biologist, so he did not say quite that, but following him we would have to conclude that the mice or the flies we catch are only imperfect copies of the one ideal Mouse or the ideal Fly.

This is a typological way of thinking. Though most biologists and anthropologists and scientists in general do not subscribe to Plato's philosophy, not a few of them approach their studies, without realizing this, as typologists. They concede that every person is different from every other, and that any mouse and any fly is not quite like any other mouse or fly. But it is so tempting to assume that all these variations among flies and mice and men are superficial appearances only, and that one can get a pretty good idea of what a "normal" fly, or mouse, or man is or should be. This way of thinking entails practical consequences, some of them of doubtful merit. Many things in our society, from foods to medicines to education, are tailored for somebody assumed to be the "normal" man. This is not satisfactory for those who are not quite "normal"—too tall or too short, too bright or a bit dull, too sensitive or too heavy-footed.

Other philosophers, some of them known as existentialists, lay great stress on human individuality. I am, and so is every other human, a unique and unrepeatable person, and not a kind of a shadow of some Universal Man. In biology, this philosophical attitude is reflected in the populational approach, which considers the differences among people and the variations among individual animals and plants to be very real and important, not just appearances or accidents or imperfections. In any case, there is conclusive evidence not only of the multiplicity of human natures, but, in fact, of the singularity of almost every individual human nature (see however identical twins).

Human body cells contain, as stated in Chapter 1, forty-six chromosomes (Figure 7), and sex cells twenty-three chromosomes. Among the forty-six chromosomes, there can be distinguished by their shapes and relative sizes in microscopic preparations several distinctive kinds; in all, there are twenty-three different pairs, the members of which are drawn side by side and numbered in the lower part of Figure 7. The sex cells contain one member of

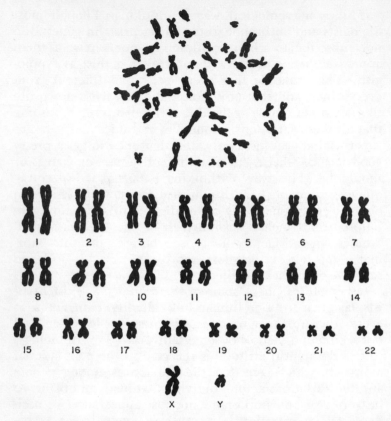

Figure 7. Human chromosomes. The 46 chromosomes as they appear in a dividing cell are shown above. The 23 pairs of the chromosomes are drawn separately in the lower part of the figure, the two members of each pair being shown side by side. The lowest, twenty-third, pair consists of two unequal partners, the X-chromosome and the Y-chromosome, in cells of male individuals. In female cells this pair consists of two X-chromosomes, and the Y-chromosome is absent. (Courtesy of Prof. Alexander G. Bearn)

each of the twenty-three pairs found in body cells. Different chromosomes carry different genes; one pair of the chromosomes, called the X and the Y, determine sex. When an egg cell unites at fertilization with a spermatozoon, the resulting fertilized egg and the cells of the body arising from it have forty-six chromosomes. Or, to be more precise, these cells have twenty-three pairs of chromosomes, since each of the twenty-three chromosomes from the mother is matched by one of a similar kind and shape from the father. The sex chromosomes in the human female are a matched pair, two X-chromosomes, while in the human male this pair consists of one X-chromosome, which is larger, and its partner, the Y-chromosome. Two X-chromosomes make a girl, one X and one Y make a boy. A boy inherits his X-chromosome from his mother, his Y from his father (see page 17).

Consider now what happens when a body with forty-six chromosomes (twenty-three pairs) in each cell has to form sex cells with twenty-three chromosomes. The formation of the sex cells, as previously stated (page 15), involves the process called meiosis. In the body cells in man, the homologous chromosomes, that is, the chromosomes that are members of a pair, one of maternal and the other of paternal origin, lie at random within the cell nucleus. Meiosis begins with the maternal and the paternal homologues exhibiting an attraction for each other, and coming together in pairs, called "bivalents." The twenty-three bivalents having been formed, the chromosomes split and form twenty-three "quadrivalents," that is, twenty-three quadripartite chromosomal bodies. Next come two meiotic divisions, during which the chromosomes no longer split, but the members of each quadrivalent separate, disjoin, segregate, and pass into four different cell nuclei. These nuclei contain, accordingly, twenty-three chromosomes, a single member of each pair. This important process is represented diagrammatically in Figure 8, which for simplicity shows three pairs, instead of twenty-three pairs, of chromosomes.

An important aspect of the process of meiosis, shown in Figure 8, is that each pair of chromosomes behaves independently of the other chromosome pairs. Independent assortment of the chromosomes means that, for example, the maternal partner of chromosome pair No. 1 has an equal chance to get into the same sex cell with either the maternal or the paternal partner of chromosome No. 2, or chromosome No. 3, and so on. With only three pairs of chromosomes, this gives eight different kinds of sex cells, as shown in Figure 8. With twenty-three pairs of chromosomes, as in man, there may be quite a variety of sex cells, ranging all the way from a kind with all twenty-three maternal (or, rather, grand-maternal) to one with all twenty-three paternal (grand-paternal) chromosomes. A little simple mathematics will be helpful here. With twenty-three independently assorting chromosome pairs, 2^{23} different kinds of assortments can be undergone. In other words, there can be formed 2^{23}, or 8,388,608, kinds of sex cells with different combinations of the grand-maternal and grand-paternal chromosomes. This is a number about as large as that of persons living in New York City or in London.

An individual has, however, not two, but four, grandparents. One may ask: How many different combinations of the chromosomes of the grandparents (assuming all these chromosomes to be different) can arise among siblings, children of the same pair of parents? Since each parent has a potentiality of forming as many as 2^{23} kinds of sex cells, and since every kind of egg cell stands an equal chance of being fertilized by any kind of spermatozoon, the total possible number of combinations rises to $2^{23} \times 2^{23} = 2^{46}$, which is a fourteen-place figure. To appreciate how large it is, let us recall that there are at present some three billion people living on earth, which is between 2^{31} and 2^{32}, or a small fraction of 2^{46}. This does not mean, of course, that so many different fertilized egg cells will in reality be produced, but this is the theoretically potentially possible variety.

Actually, 2^{46} is an underestimate. I have oversimplified the story by assuming that the paternal and the maternal

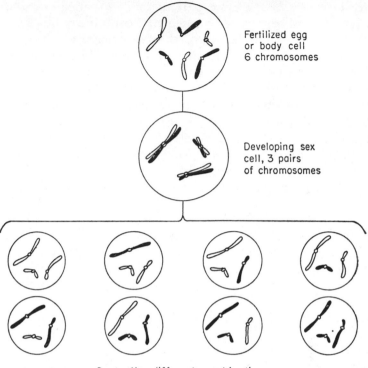

Fertilized egg
or body cell
6 chromosomes

Developing sex
cell, 3 pairs
of chromosomes

Sex cells, different combinations
of 3 chromosomes

Figure 8. A schematic representation of meiosis and sex-cell formation. A body cell is shown to contain six chromosomes, the chromosomes inherited from the mother are shown in white and those from
the father in black. At meiosis, the maternal and the paternal members of each pair come together and form three "bivalents." Eight
kinds of sex cells may then be formed, with different combinations of
the maternal and the paternal chromosomes, as shown in the lower
part of the figure.

chromosomes pair and assort as indivisible units. A
chromosome contains, however, many genes; as discovered
by Morgan and his school (see page 16), during the process
of meiosis in the sex-cell formation, the chromosomes that

are members of the same pair undergo so-called crossing-over, that is, exchange of segments, containing blocks of many genes. Suppose, then, that the maternal and the paternal chromosome sets differ in n genes; in terms of the Mendel laws this can be stated by saying that the individual is heterozygous for n genes. The number of potentially possible sex cells then increases to 2^n. This may be a fantastically large number; if n is 100, then 2^n is a thirty-place figure. Although a single ejaculation of semen from man contains some 200,000,000 spermatozoa, this is a very small number compared to 2^{100}.

One may wonder what biological meaning these colossal figures may have in reality. They are full of meaning. In man, only identical twins may have identical heredities, because they arise from division products of the same fertilized egg cell. Siblings, brothers and sisters, share on the average 50 per cent of their genes, and differ in the other 50 per cent. Each child has 50 per cent of his genes in common with each parent; since, however, the parent transmits to his child only 50 per cent of the genes he carries, parents and children are never genetically identical. With some kinds of apogamy, parthenogenesis, and virgin birth, the whole progeny inherits all the genes of their mother. This is common in some plants and in a few animals, but does not apply to the human species. Genetically identical progeny arise also with asexual reproduction, by fission of the parental body, bud formation, and so on. Asexual reproduction is commonly found among microorganisms and other lower forms of life, but, unbelievable as it may seem, it occurs also in man. Identical, or monozygotic, twins, triplets, and other identical births arise by fission of the fertilized egg cell into two or more independently developing individuals. This is asexual reproduction of a body which had arisen, of course, by a sexual process of fertilization.

Unrelated persons, one may safely assume, have negligible chances of being identical in genetic endowments.

The genetic endowment of a person is his biological nature. Every human being has, then, his own nature, individual and nonrepeatable. The nature of man as a species resolves itself into a great multitude of human natures. Everybody is born with a nature that is absolutely new in the universe, and that will never appear again (identical twins and other identical multiple births, of course, excepted).

Genotype and Phenotype

Everybody then, except identical twins, has a nature different from everybody else's. A human being unquestionably is not born a *tabula rasa*, a blank slate (see page 5). This biological fact does not contradict the principle "that all men are created equal." Arguments will be presented in the next chapter to show that equality should not be confused with identity, or genetic diversity with inequality. People need not be identical twins to be equal before God, before the law, and in their rights to equality of opportunity.

Just how different human beings are made by their different natures must be investigated. Differences between individuals arise owing to their different natures, or heredities, as well as to their different environments, or nurtures. Heredity does not necessarily decree a person's fate. It may be only a conditioning, a bias, a proclivity with which a human individual enters this world. The Danish geneticist W. Johannsen suggested in 1911 that the genotype of an individual be distinguished from his phenotype, and this distinction remains basic for clear thinking about the relations between heredity and environment. In a nutshell, the genotype is the sum total of the heredity the individual has received, mainly, as shown in the foregoing chapter, in the form of DNA in the chromosomes of the sex cells. The cytoplasm may also contain some heredity determinants; if so, they are likewise constituents of the genotype. The phenotype is the appearance of the individual—the structure and functions of his body. The concept of the phenotype subsumes, of course, not only the external appearance, but also the physiological, normal and pathological, psychological, socio-cultural, and all other characteristics of the individual.

It is often stated that the genotype of an individual is set at fertilization and does not change during an individual's lifetime. It is also said that the genotype is somehow isolated from the environment. These are shorthand metaphors which are liable to be misunderstood. The genes an individual received from his parents in the sex cells have many times replicated themselves as the fertilized egg became two, four, eight, and finally billions of cells. Surely, then, I do not have the genes I inherited from my parents; I do, however, have numerous true copies of the genes with which I started my existence. To replicate themselves, the genes must certainly interact with their environment—the copies of the genes can only be built from materials taken from the environment. The interaction is, however, a circular process—genes make more of themselves.

The phenotype, in contrast to the genotype, changes all the time, and its changes are directional rather than cyclic. I am certainly different at present from what I was in the embryonic state, or in infancy, or as a youth; if I live longer, I shall change further. A human egg cell weighs roughly one twenty-millionth of an ounce; a spermatozoon weighs much less; an adult person weighs, let us say, 160 pounds, or some fifty billion times more than an egg cell. The material for this growth comes evidently from the environment. In a broad sense, this is the food the organism consumes and transforms into constituents of the body. A human body transforms its food in ways somewhat different from a dog's or a frog's or a fly's body. The transformations occur according to the instructions emanating from the genes, by way of the DNA-RNA-ribosomes-proteins chain of command, as outlined briefly in the foregoing chapter. The outcome of the transformation depends, however, not only on the genes, but also on the materials to be transformed, that is, on the kind of food the organism consumes and on the conditions under which it develops.

The phenotype is, then, a result of interactions between the genotype and the sequence of the environments in which the individual lives. It is also said that the genotype determines the "norm of reaction" of the organism. This should not be understood to mean that some reactions of the organism are somehow intrinsically normal and others abnormal; the "norm of reaction" is simply the sum total of developmental responses which a carrier of a certain genotype might give in all possible environments, natural or artificial, favorable or unfavorable. My present phenotype, what I am as an organism and as a human being, has been determined by my genotype and by the whole succession of the environments I have encountered in my life. The "environments" include, of course, everything that can influence man in any way. They include the physical environment—climate, soil, nutrition—and, most important in human development, the cultural environment—all that a person learns, gains, or suffers in his relations with other people in the family, community, and society to which he belongs.

Genetics of Social Inequality

The existence of glaring social inequalities is often felt to be in need of justification. In some societies with such class or caste inequalities a belief is widely held, by the privileged as well as by the underprivileged, that the social stratification reflects biological, genetic, differences in human quality. The class privilege is hereditary, so the argument goes, because human ability is also hereditary. A scientific sanction for this argument becomes desirable, especially when the established order begins to be questioned by those lacking the favored status. It is probably not accidental that the pioneering studies on human heredity were undertaken in Victorian England, well in advance of the development of Mendelian genetics and of the formulation of the genotype and phenotype concepts by Johannsen. The pioneer was Sir Francis Galton, a cousin and one of the early followers of Darwin.

In 1869, Galton published a book entitled *Hereditary Genius*. The category of "genius" was made rather generously inclusive. Galton assembled a large collection of pedigrees of persons who had achieved "eminence" in various fields of activity—statesmen, jurists, scientists, poets, clergymen, military and naval commanders, and so on. Everywhere he found that the incidence of eminent people among the ancestors and relatives of these persons was far greater than in the general population of England. The conclusion drawn by Galton was that, in the development of human abilities, the nature (which is what we would now call the genotype) was far more important than the nurture (environment).

In the United States, the problem assumed in Galton's time a rather different color. Here many self-made and self-reliant men were achieving ever-greater independence, respectability, and prosperity. The optimistic creed of the Age of Enlightenment, that men in general are good by nature and need only to have their good potentialities evoked by good opportunity, seemed to be borne out by the experiences of the European white man transplanted to the wide-open spaces of the New World. But there were some annoying exceptions. Some people living by crime and in poverty and degradation failed to respond to the stimuli of opportunity. Were these dregs of society the genetic counterparts, in contrast to Galton's eminent men? The 1875 study by R. L. Dugdale seemed to suggest exactly that. He attempted to trace the pedigrees of a group of families to whom he gave the pseudonym Jukes. The ancestor of the

Jukes was a certain Max, who lived in the eastern United States in colonial days. Among some 709 of his descendants, Dugdale found 76 convicted criminals, 128 prostitutes, 18 brothel keepers, and over 200 paupers. In 1912 came H. H. Goddard's similar study on the group of families given the pseudonym Kallikak. These families were traced to a person called the "Old Horror," born during the American Revolution. Among his 480 known descendants, there were 143 feeble-minded, 24 alcoholics, 26 illegitimate children, 3 criminals, 33 prostitutes and other sexually immoral individuals.

The ghastly stories of the Jukes and Kallikaks, even more than Galton's accounts of the families of notables, made a great impression on the public in America and in Europe. The closing decades of the nineteenth and approximately the first quarter or third of the twentieth centuries were the periods of the greatest vogue of social Darwinism —a social philosophy for which Darwin was hardly responsible, but which claimed to be simply a straightforward application of Darwin's theory of biological evolution to human society. Darwin saw the biological evolution promoted by the "survival of the fittest" in the "struggle for existence." We shall see in more detail in Chapter 5 that Darwin used these expressions largely as metaphors, but there was nothing metaphorical about them to social Darwinists. Human society is a field of remorseless struggle, in which the best win, the worst lose, and the result is progress.

Herbert Spencer (1820-1903) thought that, with men or with animals, "If they are sufficiently complete to live, they do live, and it is well they should live. If they are not sufficiently complete to live, they die, and it is best they should die." The Yale University sociologist William Graham Sumner (1840-1910) thought that "poverty belongs to the struggle for existence, and we are all born into that struggle." The gist of his book entitled *What Social Classes Owe to Each Other* can be summed up simply—nothing at all! To a social Darwinist it is plain that social problems such as crime, poverty, and ignorance stem not from any defects of social organization but simply from defective genes. This view pleased greatly, and still continues to please, holders of stoutly conservative political opinions, down to Barry Goldwater.

Liberals and radicals recoiled from social Darwinism in horror. They did not, however, realize that the scientific foundations of social Darwinism fall somewhat short of imposing, and that the view which regards social problems as reducible to genetics is far from proved. They wanted the environment and social reform to be all-powerful, and they came to distrust all genetic conditioning of human traits. The result was that the stand a person took on the nature-nurture problem merely reflected his political convictions. This is surely contrary to the most elementary principle of scientific method—that any investigator who makes the same observations and experiments under similar conditions will obtain the same results, and consequently will have to reach the same conclusions.

Partitioning the Genetic and Environmental Effects

The development of genetics has ushered in more critical methods and attitudes toward studies on human heredity. Similarity between members of a family in certain characteristics is no proof that this characteristic is inherited. It is certainly helpful to have a general or an admiral for a father or a relative if one chooses a military or a naval career, or an influential politician to help a career in politics. It does not take much discernment to see that growing up in surroundings of affluence is more propitious for the development of different tastes and attitudes than growing up among paupers. This simple consideration certainly did not escape Galton's attention; Galton was, however, firmly convinced that had his eminent personalities been born among paupers they would have struggled successfully to reach their eminence. Regrettably, this conviction is simply not subject to verification.

If everybody were growing up and living in a uniform environment, under conditions of perfect equality of opportunity, then, and only then, could one be certain that the differences among people would be due to their hereditary natures. Surely, this condition is nowhere fulfilled in reality. A descendant of the Jukes or the Kallikaks, growing as a youngster among paupers and criminals, is likely to be more susceptible to the lures of violence and ill-gotten money, and less prone to seek to ameliorate his station by honest toil, than somebody who is brought up to abhor wrongdoing and vice.

Furthermore, it gradually came to be recognized that the question whether the nature or the nurture, the genotype or the environment, is more important in shaping man's physique and his personality is simply fallacious and misleading. The genotype and the environment are equally important, because both are indispensable. There is no organism without genes, and any genotype can act only in some environment. The nature-nurture problem is nevertheless far from meaningless. Asking right questions is, in science, often a large step toward obtaining right answers. The question about the roles of the genotype and the environment in human development must be posed thus: To what extent are the *differences* observed among people conditioned by the differences of their genotypes and by the differences between the environments in which people were born, grew, and were brought up?

The insistence on stating the nature-nurture problem in just this way is neither pedantry nor hairsplitting. The dichotomy of genetic and environmental traits is a false one because any trait is both genetic and environmental. I choose deliberately two farfetched examples to illustrate this proposition. Surely, the presence in man of two eyes, instead of only one, is a "hereditary" trait—it is a characteristic of the human species, of the class of mammals, and even of most representatives of vertebrate animals. Yet cases are recorded of the birth of so-called cyclopic monsters, with only one eye. Developmental accidents can cause the appearance of this monstrosity, and the cyclopic monsters have been induced experimentally in animal materials. Consider now the ability to play the game of chess. Surely it is due to human genes, since no animal other than man plays chess. Just as surely, it is environmental, since nobody plays this game in countries where it has not been introduced. However, where chess is known, some people play it well and others do not play, or play it badly. It is not pointless to ask to what extent these *differences* are due to genetic predisposition and to environmental opportunity. (This question has not, to my knowledge, been investigated.)

If the nature-nurture problem is stated correctly, the answer turns out to depend on which differences, in what particular features or characters or traits, are considered. For example, there are four blood types among people, called types O, A, B, and AB. A competent technician can take a drop of a person's blood and in a few minutes make the tests needed to determine the blood type (Figure 9). Knowing one's blood type may be important if a blood transfusion is needed. Giving A, B, or AB blood to an O blood recipient may lead to grave or even fatal consequences. Now, the blood type of an individual is already determinable in a fetus, starting with the second or third month of pregnancy; it persists unchanged during the whole life, regardless of age, state of health, or conditions of living. The blood type is inherited according to Mendel's law. There is no known way of changing the blood type with which a person is born. It is fair to say that the differences among people in their blood types are rigidly determined by their genes.

By contrast, the language a person speaks comes from his environment, not from his genes. Note, however, that the ability to learn a language, any language, is genetic; some

Anti-B serum   Anti-A serum

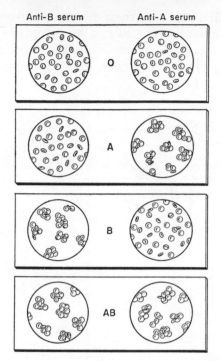

Figure 9. The tests to determine the blood type of a given person. A small amount of blood is mixed with each of two sera, the anti-A and the anti-B. The red blood cells either do, or do not, become clumped (agglutinated), depending on the blood type to which the person tested belongs.

genetic defects make a child unable to learn to speak any language. Most human differences lie between the extremes of the rigid genetic and a purely environmental causation. To estimate the relative magnitudes of the genetic and environmental influences more precisely often turns out to be exceedingly difficult. This matter obviously needs much further research.

Let us make it very clear where the difficulty lies. With plants, or animals, or microorganisms, the problem can be solved relatively more easily than it can be in man.

Different individuals, or their progenies, are raised in as uniform an environment as can be achieved, controlling the temperature, light, humidity, food, or soil in which the experimental organism grows. The differences observed

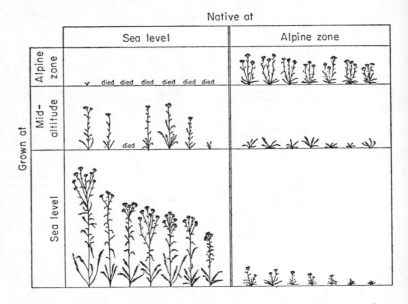

Figure 10. The yarrow plants (*Achillea*) native at sea level and at high elevations in the Sierra Nevada Mountains of California. The sea-level form dies if planted at high elevations in the Alpine Zone, and develops poorly if planted at intermediate elevations in the mountains. The Alpine Zone form does not grow well at sea level or at intermediate elevations. The differences between the varieties native at low and at high elevations are owing to genes, those between the individuals of the same variety planted at different elevations are environmental.

between the phenotypes of the individuals thus obtained depend on their genotypes being different. Or vice versa, one can take individuals having the same or very similar genotypes, and have them develop in different environments. This will yield information concerning the degree of the developmental plasticity of the organism or character in question—how great a variety of phenotypes can be obtained by having the carriers of similar genotypes brought up in different environments.

Beautiful experiments of the above kind were carried out on several species of plants by a group of investigators working at the Department of Plant Biology of the Carnegie Institution of Washington (J. Clausen, D. D. Keck, and W. M. Hiesey). Figure 10 summarizes the results of experiments on the yarrow (*Achillea*). In California, this plant grows from sea level up to the alpine zone of the Sierra Nevada Mountains. The race growing at sea level grows much taller (lower left in Figure 10) than the race native to the alpine zone (upper right in Figure 10). The young plants can be cut in several parts, and the cuttings replanted in locations of the experimenter's choice. The parts of the body of the same individual have presumably the same genotype. Now, the sea-level race planted in the alpine zone fails to survive the rigor of the climate; planted in a locality at an intermediate altitude (4,800 feet) it usually survives but does more poorly than in its native habitat. The alpine race, on the contrary, develops better in its native environment than lower down in the mountains or at sea level. In Figure 10 the vertical rows thus show the phenotypes that the same genotype engenders in different environments, while the horizontal rows show the reactions of different genotypes to similar environments.

Twins

Experiments of the above sort, quite obviously, cannot be done with humans. It is extremely difficult even to arrange for two or several persons to be brought up from infancy to maturity in identical, or even in very similar, environments. All this does not prevent some people from holding very firmly set opinions regarding what heredity or environment can or cannot do. Fortunately, the problem, though certainly difficult, need not remain insoluble forever. Nature has provided an opportunity that can be utilized to obtain some accurately verifiable information.

Identical, or monosygotic, twins arise, as indicated on page 48, through the division of a single fertilized egg into two parts, which develop into separate individuals. Identical twins are, of course, always of the same sex; barring mutation (see Chapter 4), and possibly an unequal distribution of hereditary determinants in the egg cytoplasm, they have identical genotypes. Fraternal, or dizygotic twins, come from two simultaneously maturing egg cells fertilized by two different spermatozoa. They may be either of the same or of different sexes, and they are genotypically as different on the average as brothers and sisters who are not twins. The differences that can be observed between growing or grown-up identical twins are due largely to environmental influences. The differences between fraternal twins of the same sex provide a control experiment, showing the combined effects of the genotype plus the environmental influences. Particularly valuable, but regrettably rare from a scientific point of view, are instances of twins separated at as early an age as possible and brought up apart from each other in different environments. Such twins reared apart, and especially if reared in substantially different environments, would be analogous to the yarrow plants in the experiments described above; the study of such twins could furnish invaluable information on just how plastic the human development really is.

Many observations on twins have accumulated in the genetic literature, and yet, it must be pointed out again, further research in this field is necessary if the problem of the gene-environment interaction in man is to be advanced toward a more adequate understanding. For the time being one can draw only tentative conclusions, which will almost certainly stand in need of correction when better data become available. As a broad generalization, the study of twins shows that human variation in almost every character is due in part to a genetic diversity and in part to environmental dissimilarity. Different traits are, however, quite different in this respect. The genetic component is responsible for the human diversity in some traits to a much greater extent than in other traits, and the same is true of the environmental component.

By and large, such traits as the facial features, eye and hair colors and forms, and other external traits by which we usually recognize and distinguish persons whom we meet are strongly influenced by the genotype. This is the reason why monozygotic twins are so astonishingly similar in appearance as to deserve the name "identical." Countless stories (some fictional, others quite genuine) are told about twins being misidentified, or substituted one for the other; a girl who did not know that she had a twin sister was startled to meet her double, and so on. Fraternal twins differ in facial features and other external bodily traits about as much as do brothers and sisters who are not twins.

The susceptibility to some infectious diseases is genetically conditioned. Tuberculosis (consumption) is due to the invasion of the organism by certain bacteria (Koch's bacilli). It is, then, an "environmental," not a "hereditary" disease. An individual cannot contract it unless exposed to infection. However, especially in the slums of crowded cities, everybody is exposed to some degree. Whether a person, under these conditions, develops a clinical case of tuberculosis turns out to be influenced by his heredity. F. J. Kallman and D. Reisner studied seventy-eight monozygotic twin pairs one member of which was known to have tuberculosis, and found that forty-eight of the co-twins were also tubercular. This is usually expressed by saying that 61.5 per cent (forty-eight out of seventy-eight) of the twin pairs were "concordant." Among dizygotic twins about 18 per cent, among full siblings 19 per cent, and among half-siblings 9.5 per cent were concordant. The incidence of tuberculosis in the population from which the twins came was between 1 and 1.5 per cent.

Malaria is another infectious disease, caused by a parasite infecting the red blood cells. In many tropical and subtropical countries, certain districts are, or until recently were, heavily malarial, so much so that practically the entire population was infected at some period of their lives. Several genetic conditions (sickle cells, thalassemia, G6PD deficiency, see below) have recently been proved, or suspected, to confer an at least relative resistance to certain species of the malarial parasite.

Much discussion and polemics have centered on the problem of the inheritance of intelligence. Psychologists and educationists have worked out a technique of estimation of the so-called intelligence quotient, or I.Q. What is measured by the I.Q. is not necessarily the same as what is referred to in everyday language as intelligence, cleverness, aptitude, or wit. Still less does the I.Q. give an estimate of the value or worth of the person. The I.Q. as administered to school children is regarded as a measure of their ability to handle verbal symbols. This ability shows a fairly high correlation with scholastic success, and this is what makes the I.Q. measurements useful, but at the same time suggests the limitations of their usefulness. The I.Q. is certainly not independent of the environment, of the family background, schooling, and the circumstances under which the test is administered.

Identical twins perform appreciably more similarly in intelligence tests than do fraternal twins, and the latter only slightly more similarly than do siblings who are not twins. L. Erlenmeyer-Kimling and L. F. Jarvik have recently reviewed and summarized the data obtained in fifty-two different studies by different investigators. The mean correlation coefficient for the I.Q. scores of identical twins reared together is 0.87, and for those reared apart 0.75. A correlation coefficient of 1.00 would mean that the I.Q. measurement was absolutely precise and that the variations observed are entirely genotypic and not environmental. This is obviously not so, and particularly the fact that the twins reared apart show a lower correlation than those reared together is evidence that the I.Q. depends in part on environment. However, the fraternal twins give a correlation of only 0.53, the value being almost the same for twins reared together and those reared apart. This value, 0.53, is only slightly greater than the 0.49 for siblings, brothers or sisters who are not twins, and significantly lower than the values for identical twins reared either together or apart. Important additional evidence comes from studies on the I.Q.'s of genetically unrelated persons reared together, such as children brought up in the same orphanage or foster home. Here the correlation falls to 0.23. The correlation between foster children and foster parents is only 0.20. The value of 0 would indicate, of course, no correlation at all.

The conclusion is inevitable that the performance on I.Q. tests is determined jointly by genotypic and environmental variables. The genetic component is, for this trait, appreciably greater than the environmental component in the materials covered by the studies. This last qualification is necessary and important. The point is this: Every one of the fifty-odd studies concerned itself with twins, or siblings, or foster children in the same country and usually within a rather limited section of the same country. The range of the environments to which the individuals studied were exposed was accordingly a limited one, much more limited than it could be if the persons reared apart were brought up in, for example, a Western country, China, or an Indian tribe, or at least in different social classes and different economic and educational groups. It is, indeed, evident that the more uniform the environment is the greater, relatively, is the role of genotype differences, and vice versa.

Intelligence, or whatever it is that the I.Q. scores measure, is an important but certainly not the only quality in which we are interested in our fellow men. Temperamental, emotional, and other personality traits may for some purposes and under some circumstances be equally or even more important. The handicap that has impeded scientific study of personality traits is the difficulty of reliably measuring them. Psychologists have, however, been making progress with such measurements, by means of a variety of questionnaires, personality inventories, projective tests, and so on. It is too early at present to reach firm conclusions in this difficult field. It is nevertheless interesting to quote some of the results of the recent work of I. I. Gottesman (1963), who has administered the so-called Minnesota Multiphasic Personality Inventory (MMPI) and Cattell's High School Personality Questionnaire (HSPQ) to thirty-four pairs of monozygotic and an equal number of dizygotic teen-age twins. Gottesman divides the "factors" and "test dimensions" he has measured into the following groups, according to whether the observed variation is due chiefly to genotypic or to environmental causes:

I. EQUAL CONTRIBUTIONS OF HEREDITY AND ENVIRONMENT
   Confident Adequacy versus Guilt Proneness
   Depression
   Psychopathic Deviate

II. HEREDITY PREDOMINANT
    Social Introversion

III. ENVIRONMENT PREDOMINANT
     Submissiveness versus Dominance
     Shy, Sensitive versus Adventurous
     Liking Group Action versus Fastidiously
         Individualistic Psychasthenia

One can only agree with Gottesman's following conclusion: "Granting that the difficulties of accurately assessing the contribution of heredity to variation of socially important behavior are great, such efforts will not have been in vain if they contribute to a greater understanding of the sources of individual differences. The provision of an optium environment for the optimum development of the various aspects of human behavior should follow such increased understanding."

What the Data on Twins Do Not Mean

Notwithstanding all their weaknesses and incompleteness, the studies of twins have laid a firm foundation on which to build an understanding of the roles of genotypic and environmental variables in human development. It is fair, I think, to say that, as a general rule, whenever a variable human trait, whether structural or physiological or psychological, was at all adequately studied, both genotypic and environmental causes proved to be involved to some extent. Any way you look at it, man is a creature of both his nature and his nurture. It is folly to disregard either.

Many social scientists, and also followers of some schools of psychoanalysis, feel nevertheless a compulsive distrust of any genetic determinism in man. When the evidence becomes overwhelming they try to patch things up by saying that the genetic differences between persons are, after all, very small. For example: "In a consideration of behavioral differences among people, therefore, we may regard the biological factor as a constant, and hence eliminate it from our calculations" (L. White). I can understand (and perhaps forgive) statements of this sort only as a reaction against the excesses of social Darwinists; scientists should, however, resist the temptation to oppose exaggerations by making exaggerations opposite in sign. It has, to be sure, been claimed that the studies on identical and fraternal twins prove that what man is or can become is settled and predestined by his heredity. Environment matters little; heredity is the "dice of destiny."

To bring the issue to a focus, let us consider two examples of studies of twins; one of these studies has actually been misinterpreted, while the other is easily susceptible to misinterpretation. Several investigators sought to locate in prisons individuals sentenced for a variety of offenses and who had twin brothers. It did not matter what sort of crime the individual had committed. The question asked was simply whether the twin brother did or did not have a criminal record. When each twin had a criminal record, they were called "concordant"; when the brother of the imprisoned twin was found not to have an official criminal record, the twins were "discordant." Some of the twins were monozygotic and others dizygotic; the crucial fact ascertained by the investigation was that the monozygotic twins were concordant more often than the dizygotic ones, and the difference was large enough to be statistically assured. The other study arose as a by-product of the observation that lung cancer is found more often among cigarette smokers than among nonsmokers. The suggestion was then made by an eminent geneticist that the tendency to smoke may be genetically conditioned, and that the proneness to lung cancer may be a by-product of the same genotypes. An attempt was accordingly made to examine the tobacco-smoking habits of some pairs of monozygotic and dizygotic twins. With respect to this characteristic, too, the monozygotic twins were concordant more often than the dizygotic ones.

One of the investigators of the criminality in twins, J. Lange, has published his work in a book suggestively entitled *Crime and Destiny*. We are entitled, however, to ask the question whether the information collected warrants the conclusion that some people are destined by their heredities to be criminals and others law-abiding, some to be smokers and others nonsmokers. Surely, nobody can be a tobacco smoker if he has no access to tobacco. On the other hand, some people become smokers because among their friends and acquaintances it is considered smart or "masculine" to smoke. Whether or not a person becomes a criminal, and, if so, what kind of crime he commits, and if he commits a crime whether or not he is apprehended, all this evidently depends on the kind of laws the society in which he lives has instituted, and on the strictness of the law enforcement.

Nothing whatever in the data on the "criminal" twins proves that these people would have been criminals if they had been brought up differently. For all that the data tell us, these criminals might have been Galton's eminent men, righteous pillars of society and even prosecutors of criminals. And there is nothing to show that the present pillars of society could not have been like the Jukes or Kallikaks under other circumstances. However, the data are far from meaningless; they do show that in some environments, and presumably in any environment, persons with similar genotypes are likely to be on the average more similar in their behavior than persons with different hereditary endowments. Heredity is not the destiny that foreordains that a person will behave in a certain way regardless of circumstances. Heredity does predispose him to behave this way, rather than that way, under a given set of circumstances. It is a conditioning that to a certain extent biases man's choices and efforts of will.

As stated previously, certain people like to exaggerate the deterministic role of heredity and to underestimate that of environment. Others are loath to believe that heredity can have any influence, at least on socially significant human qualities, such as intelligence and character. The antihereditarians fear that if the genes are shown to have anything to do with man's behavior, this will deprive us of our freedom, make us mere automata, and render futile all attempts to improve man by education and social betterment. These fears go hand in hand with a misunderstanding of what heredity really "determines." It has been said before, but it will bear repetition, that heredity, the genotype, the genes do not determine "characters," such as proneness to criminality or smoking habits; the genes determine the reactions of the organism to its environment.

Environmental Engineering

Any trait or character, external or internal, physiological or psychological, is, at least in principle, modifiable and governable by genetic as well as by environmental influences (Figure 11). To be sure, one cannot, at least at present, change the blood type that one's genes have determined. There are many hereditary diseases for which no remedies are known. It does not, however, follow that a hereditary, gene-controlled disease is necessarily an incurable disease. This notion is as widespread as it is misleading.

This matter is so important that we shall consider several examples, endeavoring to make it as clear as possible. Retinoblastoma is a kind of cancer of the eye that is, at least in some cases, due to a Mendelian dominant gene. The illness appears in infancy and is usually fatal; a surgical removal of the afflicted eye can save the life of the child, although it leaves him, of course, blind. The surgery, therefore, is here able to correct for a genetic defect, to the extent of saving a life that would be forfeited without the surgical intervention. Better techniques of treating this genetic disease may, of course, be invented. Dr. Kytja Voeller informs me of hopeful results of some experiments with so-called cryosurgery, selectively freezing and thus destroying the affected portion of the eye but leaving the eye as a whole still able to function.

With the progress of medicine, more and more genetic defects, which without treatment would cause death or physical or mental disability, can be alleviated, helping the patient and his family to lead happier and more useful lives. Galactosemia is a fortunately rare disease of infants, due to a Mendelian recessive gene inherited from both parents. These infants lack in their tissues an enzyme with the formidable name Gal-I-P uridyl transferase, which is

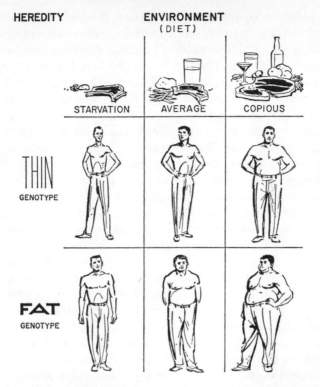

Figure 11. The heredity and the environment jointly determine how the organism develops. Some heredities (genotypes) predispose their carriers to gain weight more or less easily; but the actual weight and the appearance (phenotype) of a person depend also upon the environment in which he lives, the abundance or scarcity of food being obviously relevant.

needed to utilize the milk sugar galactose, and which is normally present in other infants. The absence of the enzyme results in accumulation of the galactose in the blood, liver damage, mental retardation, convulsions, and often in death. If the galactosemia is discovered and correctly diagnosed early enough, eliminating the galactose from the diet usually gives a considerable improvement of physical and mental development.

Another rare recessive hereditary disease of children is called acrodermatitis enteropathica. Without treatment, death is almost inevitable. The drug di-iodohydroxyquin-oline not only permits the life to be saved, but, remarkably enough, gives an ostensibly complete cure. Some forms of diabetes, a common disease, especially of old age, are also believed to be inherited through a recessive gene. The disease, though not necessarily fatal, is often more or less incapacitating. Regular injections of the hormone insulin keep many diabetics in reasonably good health. And, finally, consider another, still more common, defect, some forms of which are genetically conditioned—myopia, or shortsightedness. The corrective treatment has been known for several centuries; it is, wearing properly made glasses.

To "cure" a hereditary disease obviously does not mean removing the genes that cause it. A person with retinoblastoma whose life has been saved by timely surgery may transmit retinoblastoma to about one half of his offspring. Diabetes returns if insulin injections are withheld and the diabetic is not careful with his diet. Nearsightedness returns as soon as the nearsighted person takes off his glasses. However, the statement that a person is healthy or ill refers to his phenotype, which is observed, not to his genes, which are not visible. When a patient consults his doctor about some condition that troubles him, he does not ask the doctor to change his genes, which the doctor is utterly unable to do, only to advise him on how to change his environment in such a way that the genes with which he was born will be helped to produce a satisfactory phenotype.

Neither genetic health nor genetic disease can be defined except in terms of its opposite. And although "genetic" refers to something in the genotype, health and disease are observable only in the phenotype. If the environment in which people live were the same everywhere and could not be altered, one might conceivably select the one healthy genotype; all other genotypes would, by definition, contain genetic defects. Even then the selection would be difficult because it would involve a value judgment on which agreement would not be easy to reach. Is the optimum genotype the one giving to its carriers the greatest euphoria, or the highest working capacity, or the aesthetically most pleasing appearance, or the longest life?

In reality, the environments in which people live are not only infinitely variable, but man is able, through his technology, to devise new ones according to his specifications. A genetic endowment may give different phenotypes in different environments. Some of these phenotypes may be agreeable to their possessors and acceptable to the society in which they live; they will accordingly be regarded as healthy. Other phenotypes may give discomfort or suffering to their possessors and be socially unsatisfactory; they are unhealthy or defective. The same genotype may give health in some, but cause disease or discomfort in other environments. For example, most people do not need insulin injections, because their bodies manufacture their own insulin, but diabetics are better off in an insulin-supplying environment. Myopics need an environment that gives them glasses, or else the environment of a profession such as watch repairing, in which nearsightedness is less of an obstacle.

We have seen that no two persons, and probably no two individuals of any sexually reproducing species, have the same genotype. Excepting only identical twins, a given constellation of genes occurs only once, in only a single person. The evaluation of these genotypes is most simply made according to what phenotypes they produce in ordinary, widespread, customary environments in which most people live at present on this planet. A majority of these genotypes belong to what is described as *l'homme moyen sensuel,* the happy average, neither a giant nor a dwarf, neither completely resistant nor easily succumbing to the shocks unavoidable in customary environments, hence ordinarily enjoying a robust to good to fair health, neither a hero nor a villain, in short, the general public. This multitude of genotypes, and of phenotypes, constitutes the adaptive norm of mankind, the human species.

In addition to the adaptive norm, there is a minority of genotypes that are free of overt defects, and in addition can do in some respects much better than the norm; this is the genetic elite. And there is another minority that, in ordinary environments, develops weak or infirm bodies or minds, described as hereditary diseases, malformations, or constitutional weaknesses. This is the genetic load, or the genetic burden, which our species, like other living species, always carries. Further discussion of the problem of the genetic load will be found particularly in Chapters 4 and 5. To forestall a possible misunderstanding, it must, however, be stressed that the categories of the adaptive norm, genetic elite, and genetic load are not fixed or unchangeable forever. They depend on the environments and, in man, on social requirements. Let us be reminded that the curability or incurability of a disease has little to do with its genetic or nongenetic origin. At the present level of advancement of the medical arts there are, unfortunately, many as yet incurable environmental as well as genetic diseases. In principle, no disease need be incurable, but medicine is certainly far from having achieved a level of knowledge that would make all human suffering remediable.

Molecular and Organismic Genetics

If mankind succeeds in improving genetics, genetics may succeed in improving mankind. The ways to improve the human lot generally fall into two broad categories: environmental engineering, or euthenics, and genetic engineering, or eugenics. Methods of making better environments range from spiritual and cultural uplift, political and social reforms, improved education, and superior medical care to better nutrition and sanitation. Environments can be said to have been improved if the existing array of human

genotypes reacts to these environments by developing
healthier, happier, or in some other ways more desirable or
admirable phenotypes. On the other hand, one may endeavor to improve the array of human genetic endowments. Measures may be taken to prevent the formation of
genotypes that are environmentally refractory, that react
badly to most existing or easily contrived environments.
This is negative eugenics. Or else, one may seek to encourage the increase and spread of good genotypes, which react
favorably to existing environments or to environments in
the offing. This is positive eugenics.

Recent advances in genetics, in Mendelian organismic
genetics, but particularly in biochemical or molecular
genetics, are grounds for optimism. The work on heredity
coded by means of the four genetic "letters" in the DNA
chain molecules will surely abide as one of the greatest, if
not the greatest, achievement of biology in our age. The
hopes for new approaches to both euthenics and eugenics,
based on the application of the discoveries in molecular
genetics, go very far. We have seen that treatments have
already been discovered, that is, artificial environments
have been devised in which certain genotypes that in ordinary environments react by genetic disease can live fairly
happily. Insulin supplied to diabetics, withholding galactose from infants with galactosemia genes, the drug that
relieves acrodermatitis enteropathica, these and other
examples show how much can be accomplished if the
biochemical basis of the genetic defect is understood, and
measures to correct it properly applied.

It is only reasonable to expect that the knowledge of the
developmental mechanisms involved in other hereditary
diseases and malformations will progressively increase. It
may then become possible to manage their manifestation in
the phenotype. Hopefully, the carriers of defective genes
may be helped to live happy and useful lives. An even
bolder approach is conceivable. This is to control the gene
action itself at the level of the DNA-RNA-ribosome-en-

zyme chains of reactions. Evidence is rapidly growing that
the genes in the chromosomes of a cell nucleus are not
continuously active; the reactions that lead to formation of
enzymes occur only at certain stages in the development of
the body; different genes seem to be active in different cells
and at different times. Cellular mechanisms exist that cause
the action of this or that gene to be "switched on" or "off."
My colleague A. E. Mirsky has pointed out the possibility
of discovering methods to suppress the action of undesirable genes and perhaps to enhance the action of favorable
ones.

Euthenics is, however, not alternative, but complementary to eugenics. Even if we had methods available to control or to suppress the action of undesirable genes, it is
certainly better to have no need to resort to such opera-
tions. At the very best they are likely to be laborious and
costly. Geneticists have always kept in mind, even as only a
remote possibility, that someday they may be able to alter
an organism's heredity in predetermined ways. Gene
changes, mutations, occur, as will be discussed in Chapter
4, mostly "spontaneously." And most mutations are, alas,
detrimental to the organism that carries them. The word
"spontaneous" applied to a process of nature is only another way of saying that the cause or causes of the process or
event so described are unknown. The progress of molecular
genetics will, some optimists believe, change all that.

Suppose that geneticists and biochemists learn how to
extract from cells, or even to synthesize, parts of the DNA
chain molecules that act as desirable genes, and that they
learn also how to introduce these good genes into the chromosomes of human cells, replacing there some bad genes.
Such a feat or discovery is, indeed, within the range of
reasonable possibility. It is to some extent paralleled by
the "transformations" and "transductions" achieved, as
mentioned above, in some bacteria. One can take a strain of
bacteria not possessing a certain genetic property, and
introduce this property with the DNA extracted from

another strain. Directed genetic changes of this sort have also been achieved in human cells, cultivated outside the organism in tissue cultures.

None of these methods of gene "transplantation," suppression, or stimulation are as yet available for improving human heredity. Modern man is, however, so accustomed to expect science to produce "miracles" that some scientists and popular writers talk and write about them as though they were accomplished facts. A little overdose of optimism is perhaps not undesirable here and there in our Age of Anxiety; barring unforeseen calamities, new and important discoveries in biological science may confidently be anticipated. What cannot be anticipated is just what these discoveries will be, and in just what fields they will be made. It is for this reason that I wish to enter here a plea that biological research should be pursued on a broad front, and not allowed to become funneled in a single direction, no matter how promising it may seem at present to be. There is some danger of this.

The dazzling achievements of molecular genetics have captivated wide circles of biologists, chemists, and other scientists. This is all to the good. It has been stated above that these achievements are outstanding in modern biology. No informed person can gainsay this. But perhaps it is not untimely to recall that there are also other branches of biology, and that it may be well to keep them, too, in working order. There are several levels of biological integration. Living matter, like inert matter, consists of atoms and molecules. These are organized into genes, chromosomes, and other cellular organs or "organelles," which are integrated into cells. Cells compose tissues, organs, and individuals. Individuals are organized into populations and species; all humans are members of a single species mankind, *Homo sapiens*. Species are members of biotic communities, or ecosystems. It is convenient to divide these levels into two groups: the molecular level and all others, subsumed under the name organismic level. So there is molecular and organismic biology, molecular and organismic genetics.

Here is a question, which is at the same time practical and abstractly philosophical: Is it necessary and expedient to study the phenomena of life on all levels of biological integration, or is it better to concentrate on the lowest molecular level? Some hundred and twenty years ago, the French philosopher Auguste Comte propounded a hierarchy of sciences, starting with the most perfect, which he thought was mathematics, through mechanics, physics, chemistry, biology, psychology, and finally to the least-advanced one—sociology. Not all practicing scientists today, perhaps not even a majority, have heard about Comte, and even fewer have read his works (which, incidentally, make dull reading). But the Comtian hierarchy became something like a faith with most scientists; each preceding science is considered "fundamental" to the one succeeding on the list. It is believed that as a science progresses, the phenomena it studies should be explained by being reduced to those of the more fundamental level. So psychology must be reduced to biology, biology to chemistry, and so on. Organismic genetics must be reduced to molecular genetics.

Simply as a method of handling scientific data, reduction has great intrinsic merits. The discoveries of, for example, the chemical processes involved in digestion, respiration, heredity transmission, nerve conduction, and other living processes are among the great achievements of biology. The historical odds are, however, against the prospect of describing all biological, let alone psychological and sociological, phenomena in chemical and then in physical terms. This is not only because such a description would be hard to achieve, but mainly because it would be so cumbersome and inconvenient as to be meaningless. Chromosomes and cells are composed of nothing but chemical substances; there is no chromosomal entelechy and no cell psyche; but a chromosome is a chromosome and a cell is a cell because the chemical substances composing them are organized in patterns that make them functional units. Biology is a study of the patterns and units that occur only in living matter and make it alive, as well as a study of the chemical components of these patterns.

As stated on pages 37-38, biologists reject vitalism not because every single biological phenomenon has already been reduced to chemistry. It is, rather, because, to operate in a living organism, a vital force would have to be some kind of chemical substance or process. There is nevertheless an influential school of thought among scientists which contends that if one concentrates all the attention and all the research support on molecular biology and molecular genetics, then all organismic biology and genetics will somehow explain itself without need of research on the organismic level. I can scarcely imagine a contention more misconceived. The laws of Mendel, of gene segregation and recombination, are not deducible from any of the glorious achievements of chromosome and gene chemistry. And they need not be so deduced; Mendel's laws and much else in biology have been discovered through studies on the organismic level. Biology moves both downward and up-ward—from the organismic to the molecular and from the molecular to the organismic levels.

This book is about the studies of heredity that help in understanding man and his nature. Molecular genetics is certainly relevant here. To mention just one reason for this, some of the diseases to which human flesh is heir are molecular diseases. But man is an organism, not a mole-cule. Organismic genetics holds the key position among the biological sciences that endeavor to contribute to man's understanding of himself.

[III]

Race

The idea that all men are, or should be, equal is by no means new. Like many other basic ideas, it was clearly stated in ancient Greece (as was the opposite idea, that men neither are nor should be equal). Early Christianity was frankly, even forcibly, egalitarian, although some of the organized churches became caste conscious. What is new, and is in fact one of the dominant trends of our time, is that people almost everywhere now take the idea of human equality quite seriously. It is no longer accepted as Nature's law that people with darker skins are destined to be servants and those with lighter skins masters. This leads to social unrest. In a traditional class or caste society, a person of humble birth might not have been wholly happy with his status, but he at least knew what his status was to be, and was not very likely to feel frustrated or disillusioned. Not so nowadays; children of those at the bottom of the social ladder no longer acquiesce in being placed automatically in the position their parents ungrudgingly accepted.

Somehow people became convinced that everyone is equal. But what is equality? On the authority of the Declaration of Independence, it is a self-evident truth "that all men are created equal." And yet, people are demonstrably diverse biologically. Not even brothers and sisters, children of the same parents, carry the same genes (unless they are identical twins). The number of different genotypes in mankind is consequently almost equal to the number of persons living. And no matter how many people may yet be born, despite any "population explosion," a tremendous majority of the potentially possible genetic endowments will never be realized. Do biology and genetics really contradict what the Declaration of Independence holds to be a self-evident truth?

There is no contradiction; the appearance of contradiction is due to a confusion of meaning. Equality is not the same thing as identity, and inequality does not necessarily follow from diversity or variety. Geometric figures are said to be equal if they are identical in size and shape, and coincide when superimposed on each other. Human equality, whether of persons or of groups, obviously means nothing of this sort. People are genetically not all alike; this is a well-ascertained biological fact. The differences among people can be seen, measured, and studied. On the other hand, equality and inequality are not biological phenomena at all; they are political, ethical, or religious principles. Variety is a percept, what we perceive with our senses; equality is a precept, a rule of moral conduct. People are equal before God, before the law, and in their rights to life and opportunity. To be equal, people need not be alike; they need not be identical twins; unlike people are equals if the society in which they live accords to them an equality of opportunity. Brothers and sisters who are not identical twins may still share equally their patrimony. The society in which we live can grant equality to, or withhold it from, its members; it cannot make them genetically alike, even if this were desirable.

Individual and Group Diversity

Since our neighbors and even closest relatives are all genetically distinct and different persons, it is scarcely surprising that people living in remote lands, or people whose ancestors came from such lands, are more noticeably different. A problem that arises in this connection is as subtle as it may be troublesome. Intrapopulational variability, that is, the differences between individuals belonging to a group, is treated differently from interpopulational variability, the differences between groups, populations, nations, or races. The differences between individuals are usually stated in terms of their particular characteristics—one is somewhat taller, or shorter, darker or lighter, lazier or more active, kinder or more easily angered, and so on. Not so with groups; a group is usually given a name, and this name is assumed to stand for a complex of characteristics common to all members of the group. A person whose ancestors lived in America before Columbus is referred to simply as an Indian, and he whose ancestors came from tropical Africa as a Negro.

Up to a point, using group names is, of course, legitimate. People of African ancestry often have such conspicuous traits as a dark skin, kinky hair, broad nose, and full lips. Yet, individual Indians, Negroes, and persons of any other group differ from each other markedly. To name a group of people is often to create a stereotype to which most of the group's members do not respond except in part. The fewer persons of a given group one knows, the more rigid are the stereotypes one holds of what all Indians, Negroes, Irishmen, or Jews are supposed to be. A man who says that all Japanese look alike to him does not know the Japanese well.

To quote A. Rose, a sociologist: "Stereotypes take strange forms. . . . A stereotype applied to one group of people at one time may be applied to another group at a later time. In England during the seventeenth century, the

Scottish Lowlanders were stereotyped as coarse, cruel, and animal-like people. By the nineteenth century, this stereotype was applied no longer to the Scots, but to the Irish. Stereotypes can change very rapidly: in Western countries before 1940, the Japanese were thought of as sly but weak, rigid and unimaginative. After the outbreak of war with Japan in 1941 the stereotype of the Japanese still included slyness, but shifted to include toughness and resourcefulness as well. After the victory over Japan in 1945, and the beginning of a successful occupation, the stereotype dropped slyness and substituted gullibility!"

Invention and misuse of stereotypes has deep roots in the human psyche. They are specimens of misapplied typological thinking, referred to on page 43. The man in the street is, indeed, a spontaneous typologist! His stereotypes imply an unstated assumption that individual Jews are but personifications of some archetype of Jew, and individual Japanese of some archetype of Japanese. What is most unfortunate about stereotypes is not even their falsehood, though the falsehood is plain, but their consequences. Individuals, persons, are too often treated not according to the truth of what they are as individuals, but according to the stereotype of the group to which they are said to belong but to which they as persons do not in fact conform. This is as unwarrantable biologically as it is ethically iniquitous.

Species and Races As Biological Phenomena

It does not, of course, follow from the prevalence of false stereotypes of peoples that no scientific classification can be made of groups of humans or of other living things. Race is a category of classification applied to subdivisions of mankind. It is used as well to classify subdivisions of other biological species, animals and plants. Race is, however, also a biological phenomenon; there are races of man, and of animals and plants, and the races exist regardless of whether there is someone who wishes to classify them. It is important to have a clear idea of what races are, and what they are not, both as classificatory devices and as biological phenomena. Clarity is particularly important here because the race concept has suffered long from confusion. Too often some people have sought to defend the validity of certain assumptions about race, which they have accepted without proof, for opportunistic purposes or because of emotional biases.

Scientific classification of living things started with Linnaeus in the mid-eighteenth century. Between a million and a half and two million species of animals and plants have been described since Linnaeus. The exact number is hard to estimate; many new, not previously known, species are described every year. It is considered probable that there may be four million, or even more, species now living on earth. An individual animal or plant always belongs to a certain species, and not to two or more species at the same time. For example, an animal can be either a horse (*Equus caballus*) or an ass (*Equus asinus*); a species hybrid, mule, really belongs to neither species; its name, if you wish to give it in Latin, would be *Equus caballus* × *Equus asinus*. Mules are sterile, and do not form a breeding population of their own; some plant species do form hybird breeding populations, denoted "hybrid swarms." Anthropologists and biologists, when they started to describe and to classify races of men and animals and plants, treated races just as they treated species. Each race was catalogued and given a name. J. F. Blumenbach, a pioneer anthropologist, distinguished in 1775 five races: Caucasian or white, Mongolian or yellow, Ethiopian or black, American or red, and Malayan or brown.

This seemed a legitimate way to proceed. However, soon difficulties arose. Anthropologists could not agree concerning how many races there are within the human species. Blumenbach's classification had divided people according to skin color, but people differ also in many other ways— some have straight or wavy or curly or frizzy hair, narrow or broad noses; some are tall and others short; some have long and others round heads. When more and more distinguishing characteristics were taken into account, there emerged nearly as many different classifications as there were classifiers.

Thus, the Swedish anatomist G. M. Retzius thought that the shape of the skull and its parts is very important, and, in 1856, divided people into dolichocephalic (longheaded) and brachycephalic (roundheaded), prognathous (with protruding jaws or teeth) and orthognathous (straight-jawed). The shape of the head, and of the jaws, and the skin color do not necessarily go together. Europeans are light-skinned and orthognathous, but in northern Europe and in some Mediterranean countries, people are dolichocephalic, while in central Europe they are mostly brachycephalic. In Asia there are prognathous brachycephals and dolichocephals, and orthognathous dolichocephals. Africans were believed by Retzius to be dark-skinned, dolichocephalic, and prognathous.

Joseph Deniker, in 1900, distinguished the following twenty-nine "races and subraces":

A. Wooly hair, broad nose
   Yellow skin, steatopygous—Bushmen
   Dark skin—Negrito, Negro, Melanesian
B. Curly or wavy hair
   Dark skin—Ethiopian, Australian, Dravidian
   Tawny white skin—Assyroid
C. Wavy brown or black hair, dark eyes
   Clear brown skin—Indo-Afghan
   Tawny white skin—Arab or Semite, Berber, Littoral
      European, Ibero-Insular
   Dull white skin—Western European, Adriatic
D. Fair, wavy or straight hair
   Reddish white skin—Northern European, Eastern European
      ropean

E. Straight or wavy hair, dark, black eyes
   Light brown skin—Ainu
   Yellow skin—Polynesian, Indonesian, South American
F. Straight hair
   Warm yellow skin—North American, Central American, Patagonian
   Brownish yellow skin—Eskimo
   Yellowish white skin—Lapp, Ugrian, Turkish or Turco-Tatar
   Pale yellow skin—Mongol

In 1934, Egon von Eickstedt had three races: Europiform or Leucoderm (white), Negriform or Melanoderm (black), and Mongoliform or Xanthoderm (yellow), with respectively nine, eight, and twelve subraces. This adds to twenty-nine subraces, the same number as Deniker had, but they are by no means the same subraces. These examples suffice to show the utter lack of agreement between different race classifiers. What is most discouraging is not this disagreement, but the fact that the disagreement is not owing to a remediable insufficiency of information. In fact, the more carefully human populations are studied, the less clear-cut the races become. One is forced to conclude that there must be some basic fault in the methods of describing and classifying races. The difficulty is not restricted to human races; it is often met with also in zoological and botanical materials.

Biologists are not infrequently in doubt as to whether certain animals or plants should be regarded as belonging to one and the same or to two or more different species; however, with enough material, and given careful study, the doubts can usually be resolved. For example, in the western United States and British Columbia there live two species of Drosophila flies: *Drosophila pseudoobscura* and *Drosophila persimilis*. They look very much alike; in fact, males can be distinguished with difficulty by a detail in the structure of their genitalia, and females are thus far completely indistinguishable. Should they be put in one species or recognized as two species? A detailed inquiry has revealed the following facts: (1) *pseudoobscura* and *persimilis* have distinguishable chromosomes, (2) they prefer different habitats, (3) when crossed in laboratory experiments they produce completely sterile male hybrids, (4) the hybrid females, although fertile, produce constitutionally weak progenies, (5) females of either species accept males of their own species much more often than those of the other species, (6) where the two species occur in nature sharing the same territory, hybrids are extremely rare or absent. Conclusion: *Drosophila pseudoobscura* and *Drosophila persimilis* are different species.

There must be some valid biological reason why it is easier to distinguish and to delimit species than races. Such a reason does exist. Species are genetically closed systems; they do not interbreed and do not exchange genes, or do so rarely. Races are genetically open systems, and the gene exchange between them is a more or less frequent occurrence. Species do not exchange genes because they are reproductively isolated. Reproductive isolation is any genetically conditioned property that impedes or prevents miscegenation and gene exchange between populations. The reproductive-isolating mechanisms that keep separate the species *Drosophila pseudoobscura* and *Drosophila persimilis* are their preference for different habitats, the sexual (also called ethological) isolation, the sterility of male hybrids, and the weakness of the progenies of hybrid females.

The genes of the species horse (*Equus caballus*) do not diffuse into the gene pool of the species ass (*Equus asinus*), nor do genes of the latter species diffuse into the horse gene pool. Although many mules are produced, they are sterile and consequently do not constitute a channel for gene exchange. The gene pools of the species man, chimpanzee, gorilla, and orang are quite separate. It is unknown whether viable hybrids between them could be produced by artificial insemination, but even if this were possible, the hybrids would most likely be sterile. The reproductive isolation of species serves an important biological function. The genotype of each species is not just a collection of independent genes; it is a harmonious system which gives the creature the capacity to survive in certain environments. Gene exchange between such systems is likely to be unfavorable, just as exchanging parts between automobiles of different makes may not give a serviceable combination. To state the same point with a different emphasis, the biological meaning of the separation of species is evolutionary independence. Each species is adapted to its own way of life, and the evolutionary changes that take place in a species must be constructed from its own genetic materials. No matter how favorable may be a new gene arising in the human species, it will not benefit the species chimpanzee, nor vice versa. It cannot cross the reproductive-isolation barrier separating these species.

Gene Exchange between Races

The above is not so with races. They do exchange genes, or are at least potentially capable of exchanging them. The division of living things into species is more clear-cut than the further subdivision of species into races, because species have a discernible line of genetic demarcation one from the other; races do not. Mankind, the human species, was a single evolutionary unit, at least since the mid-Pleistocene period (the Ice Age). It continues to be a single unit, all segregations and apartheids notwithstanding. Wherever different human populations are sympatric, that is, geographically intermingled in a common territory as castes or as religious or linguistic groups, some miscegenation and gene exchange crops up, either openly or surreptitiously.

More important still is the interbreeding and gene flow

among populations of neighboring territories. Although man apparently always was a traveler and colonizer, it is a relative innovation in mankind that some racially distinct populations live sympatrically, as do Negroes and whites over a considerable part of the United States. It appears that before, say, 2000 B.C., the major human races, like the races of most animal species, were largely allopatric, that is, living in different countries. However, the peripheral gene flow, the gene exchange between allopatric but neighboring populations by intermarriage, is and always was a regular occurrence. This is as true of man as it is of animal or plant species. The sea-level and the alpine races of the yarrow shown in Figure 10 are quite distinct; if the populations of this plant growing at intermediate elevations are studied, they are found to be intermediate both in appearance and in their physiological properties. Figure 12 shows schematically the lines of genetic communication in the world between human populations, as envisaged by the anthropologist F. S. Hulse.

The most ancient well-documented evidence of gene exchange between human races comes from the part of

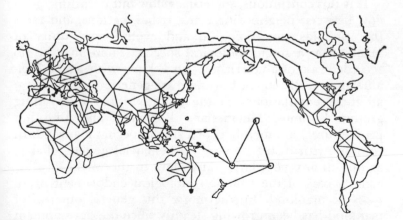

Figure 12. Lines of genetic communication between human populations of different parts of the world. (From F. S. Hulse)

Palestine that is now Israel. The Neanderthal race of mankind lived approximately between 150,000 and 40,000 years ago; remains of its bones have been found over a territory from western Europe and northern Africa to Crimea and central Asia (Turkestan). Now, in some caves on Mount Carmel, in Galilee, remains of a number of individuals have been discovered which range in their characteristics from a Neanderthaler to a modern kind of man. Surely this does not mean that the modern man arose in Palestine from a Neanderthal, nor that the remains are of progenies of mixed couples in which one member was a Neanderthal and the other modern. Far more likely, Palestine was at that time inhabited by a population about intermediate between the two races. Such intermediate populations, combining characteristics of different races, occur in animal and plant species in geographically intermediate territories between the territories of the respective races. One can see this in modern man, for example, in Egypt and the Sudan (where white and black races meet), or in western Siberia and Turkestan (where white and Mongolian races are neighbors).

It is this continuous, sometimes slow but unfailing, gene flow between neighboring clans, tribes, nations, and races that upholds the biological and evolutionary unity of mankind as a single biological species. There may be no recorded case of a marriage of an Eskimo with, say, a Melanesian or a Bushman, but there are genetic links between all these populations via the geographically intervening groups. Eskimos, Melanesians, Bushmen, and all other people surely are members of a single species, mankind. In contrast with distinct species, a beneficial genetic change arising in any population anywhere in the world may become a part of the common biological endowment of all races of mankind. Furthermore, this genetic oneness of mankind has been growing steadily since the development of material cultures has made travel and communication between the inhabitants of different countries progressively more and more rapid and easy. What should be stressed, however, is that mankind did not become a meaningful biological entity in recent generations, when men began to travel often and far. The human species was such an entity even before it became recognizably human.

Races, on the contrary, are not, and never were, clearly defined biological groups. The gene flow between human populations makes race boundaries always more or less blurred. Consider three groups of people, for example, Scandinavians, Japanese, and Congolese. Every individual in these groups will probably be easily placeable in one of three races—White, Mongoloid, or Negroid. It will, however, be far from easy to delimit these races if one observes also the inhabitants of the countries geographically intermediate between Scandinavia, Japan, and the Congo respectively. Suppose, for example, that one travels as follows: Norway-Sweden-Denmark-Germany-Switzerland-Italy-Greece-Egypt-Sudan-Kenya-Uganda-Congo. The inhabitants of each country visited are perceptibly different from those of other countries, and in fact they are different in different parts of the same country. On the whole, the populations of neighboring countries will be found to be more similar than those of countries farther apart. It is not quite accurate to say that the populations of the countries between Norway and the Congo form a perfect chain of intermediates between the extremes. The situation is really more complex than this; the geographically intermediate populations are more or less intermediate in some traits, but in other traits they may deviate in other directions from both extremes.

One may try to get out of the difficulty by recognizing several intermediate races; or else one may speculate that the races were nicely distinct at some time in the past, and got mixed up lately owing to miscegenation. This helps not at all. The more races one sets up, the fuzzier their boundaries become. And, as stated above, the difficulty is by no means confined to man; it occurs as well in many biological species where it cannot be blamed on recent miscegenation. Perhaps it is human to believe that by breaking entities down into the smallest component parts, greater understanding of the nature of reality can be achieved. But what may be true of physics, and even of biology, in, for example, a study of cellular structure, may not be true of the attempt to divide men into more and more races. Not every division theoretically conceivable and with some demonstrated justification turns out to be true, and, in science, categories are only useful when they are verified by the evidence.

Gene Frequencies

New light on the nature of races has been shed by studies on human blood types or blood groups, that is, on the chemical constituents of human blood (see page 57). Blood transfusion used to be a risky operation; some persons could accept the blood of certain other persons without injury, while with others a transfusion led to serious illness. Karl Landsteiner found in 1901 that people can be divided into four blood groups, now called Groups O, A, B, and AB, and that the red blood cells of some groups become agglutinated, that is, clumped together in the liquid part (serum) of the blood of certain other groups (Figure 9). It was eventually shown by F. Bernstein that the blood groups are inherited very simply according to Mendel's law, through three variant forms of a certain gene. Brothers and sisters, and parents and children may, and quite often do, belong to different blood groups.

During World War I, when many persons needed blood transfusions, it was discovered that the frequencies of the four blood groups are rather different in persons native to different parts of the world. Numerous investigations have been made and published since then, especially in recent years, to map the geographic distribution of blood groups (Figures 13 and 14). A total of several million people had their blood "typed." As shown in Table 2, persons of all four groups are found almost everywhere, but in different proportions. Any human race or population can be described in terms of the percentages of the blood groups. Thus B and AB blood are relatively commonest among peoples of central Asia and India, A blood in western Europe and in some American Indians, while many American Indian tribes belong predominantly or even exclusively to group O.

Several additional blood-group systems, genetically independent of the "classical" O-A-B-AB, have also been discovered. Most of them are of relatively limited practical importance, except for the Rhesus, or Rh, system. This has become widely known because couples in which the husband has so-called Rh-positive blood and the wife Rh-negative may be "Rhesus incompatible." The Rh-negative mother pregnant with an Rh-positive child may develop in her blood certain substances, antibodies, that will be injurious, particularly in subsequent pregnancies, to an Rh-positive fetus or newborn infant. There are actually not two (positive and negative), but several, variant forms of the Rh gene, symbolized by combinations of the letters C, D, and E. Examples of the frequencies of the principal variants in some human populations are shown in Table 3.

The commonest variants of the Rhesus gene in European populations are CDe and cde; the former is equally or more common in Asia, America, and Australia, but rare in Africa; the latter is commonest among the Basques (in the Pyrenees on the boundary of France and Spain), and relatively rare or absent outside Europe. The variant cDe is the commonest among the populations of Africa (south of the Sahara Desert). In a sense, this is a characteristic Negro variant. This gene does, however, occur, albeit infrequently, in human populations almost everywhere in the world, and there is no reason whatever to think that it has spread so widely owing to a Negro admixture in recent centuries.

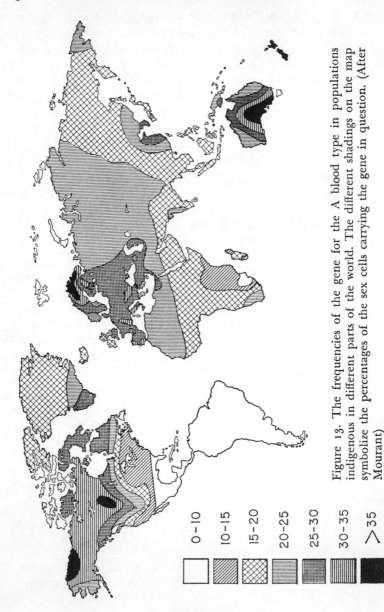

Figure 13. The frequencies of the gene for the A blood type in populations indigenous in different parts of the world. The different shadings on the map symbolize the percentages of the sex cells carrying the gene in question. (After Mourant)

0–10
10–15
15–20
20–25
25–30
30–35
>35

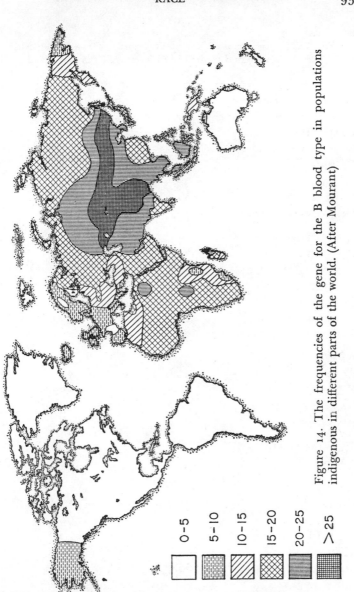

Figure 14. The frequencies of the gene for the B blood type in populations indigenous in different parts of the world. (After Mourant)

0–5

5–10

10–15

15–20

20–25

>25

TABLE 2

Frequencies, by per cent, of people belonging to the "classical"
O–A–B–AB blood groups in different parts of the world

POPULATION	O	A	B	AB
EUROPE				
SCOTTISH	51.2	34.2	11.8	2.7
FRENCH	41.6	47.0	8.0	3.3
SERBIANS	32.5	41.9	18.2	7.3
POLES	33.1	39.3	19.0	8.5
RUSSIANS (MOSCOW)	33.3	37.4	22.8	6.5
ASIA				
PERSIANS	37.9	33.3	22.2	6.6
HINDU (BOMBAY)	31.8	29.2	28.3	10.8
SIAMESE	37.3	21.8	33.1	7.8
BURIATS	30.4	21.9	37.8	9.9
CHINESE (PEKING)	28.6	26.6	32.0	12.8
JAPANESE (TOKYO)	30.1	38.4	21.9	9.7
AFRICA				
EGYPTIANS	32.6	35.5	24.4	7.5
KIKUYU (KENYA)	60.4	18.7	19.8	1.1
BANTU (S. AFRICA)	46.4	29.5	19.4	4.7
BUSHMEN	56.0	33.9	8.5	1.6
AUSTRALIA				
ABORIGINES	60.7	39.3	0	0
AMERICA				
ESKIMOS (ALASKA)	38.1	44.1	13.1	4.8
BLOOD	17.4	81.8	0	0.7
NAVAJO	72.6	26.9	0.2	0.2
MAYA	97.8	1.3	0.5	0.5
BORORO (BRAZIL)	100.0	0	0	0

TABLE 3

Frequencies, by per cents, of several more common variants of the Rhesus genes in different parts of the world

POPULATION	Gene Variants				
	CDe	Cde	cDE	cDe	cde
EUROPE					
ENGLISH	43.1	0.7	13.6	2.8	38.8
GERMANS	43.9	0.6	13.7	2.6	37.8
SPANISH	43.2	1.9	12.0	3.7	38.0
BASQUES	37.6	1.5	7.1	0.5	53.1
ASIA					
EAST PAKISTAN	63.3	6.5	7.6	3.9	17.1
SOUTH CHINESE	75.9	0	19.5	4.1	0
JAPANESE	60.2	0	30.8	0	5.3
AFRICA					
KIKUYU (KENYA)	7.3	1.4	9.9	59.5	20.4
BANTU					
(S. AFRICA)	4.7	5.8	8.5	59.6	21.4
BUSHMEN	9.0	0	2.0	89.0	0
AUSTRALIA					
ABORIGINES	56.4	12.9	20.1	8.5	0
AMERICA					
ESKIMOS	72.5	0	53.0	0	8.0
BLOOD	47.8	0	34.8	0	9.9
NAVAJO	43.1	0	27.7	28.0	0

These facts are profoundly significant. Consider the following situation, which is by no means unusual: A person of European origin, say an Englishman or a Frenchman, has O-type blood, while his brother has B blood. In this particular respect, the brothers differ from each other, while one of them resembles many American Indians with O blood, the other matches numerous persons in Asia and elsewhere who have B blood. Or else one of the brothers may have the kind of Rhesus-blood type characteristic of Africans, and the other brother may have a blood more like a majority of his European neighbors. Such characteristics, of which the persons concerned are usually quite unaware, may become vitally important in some circumstances. If an individual with O-type blood needs a blood transfusion, then O-type blood from a donor of no matter what race will be safe, while the blood of the recipient's brother may be dangerous if that brother has A, B, or AB blood. This did not prevent the following completely useless operation: during World War II, blood donations were separated by race, Negro and White. There must have been some persons with enough political "pull" who wanted to have this done, in defiance of all the evidence that what matters is not the race of the donor but his individual characteristics.

Difficulties of the Modern Concept of Race

An important conclusion must be drawn from the genetic studies of human populations: Race differences are compounded of the same genetic variables in which individuals within a race also differ. Every race includes persons with diverse genetic endowments. An individual can be understood only by observation of his own person; one learns little by noting the place of origin of his ancestors. Races can be defined as populations that differ in the frequencies or in the prevalence of certain genes. Race differences are relative, since an individual may belong to more than one race, or to no race at all; his genotype may combine genes characteristic, in a statistical sense, of different race populations. Species, when fully formed and differentiated, are not relative, but absolute, at least in the sense that a genetically effective individual belongs to one and only one species. There is no individual about whom the question could be raised as to whether he is a man, a chimpanzee, or a gorilla, even though at least one imaginative writer has published a book discussing the complications that would arise if such an individual were found.

This modern race concept, based on the findings of genetics, appears to differ so much from the traditional view that it has provoked some misunderstanding and, consequently, opposition. Is it justified to use traits like blood groups to elucidate the nature of the races of which mankind is composed? To distinguish races, should one not use traits like skin pigmentation, rather than blood groups? Persons belonging to every blood group can be found anywhere in the world; on the other hand, pale skins (other than albino) do not occur among the natives of, say, equatorial Africa or of New Guinea, and black skins are not found among the natives of Europe. This objection is beside the point. The blood types are useful not because they are the only, or the most consequential, traits in which human populations in different parts of the world differ. They are invaluable, rather, because their genetic nature is relatively simple and well understood. The classification of human races need not be, and cannot be, based on any one trait—even one like skin color, which is dramatically visible. The behavior of the blood types helps, however, to understand the behavior of all other traits.

Though not different in principle from the blood groups, the genetics of skin color and similar traits is considerably more complex. The color difference between heavily pigmented Negro and white skin is due to joint action of several genes, each of which by itself makes the skin only slightly darker or lighter. Geneticists have studied the inheritance of skin pigmentation for half a century, yet exactly how many genes are involved is still unknown. There may be as many as four or five or six main genes, genes that produce relatively large color differences, and in addition several to many genes modifying the color within narrower limits. Skin color is obviously variable among the so-called "white" as well as among the "black" peoples, some persons being darker and others lighter. Were it possible to map the geographic distribution of each separate skin-color gene as thoroughly as it has been done for some blood-group genes, race differences in color would be resolved into gene-frequency differences.

It is fair to say that the studies on blood types and similar traits have, thus far at least, helped more in the understanding of what races are than in classifying them. This is not one and the same problem. Suppose, for example, that a detailed investigation is made of the genetic differences between the populations of Norway, Italy, and Egypt. This might throw much needed light on the problem of how such genetic, racial, differences are constructed and how they arise. This may or may not, however, help to decide how many races one should distinguish in mankind, and just where the lines between these races should be drawn. The first problem is a general one—what is the nature of race differences?—the second is how most conveniently to subdivide and to name the populations of a given species.

Human populations that inhabit different countries differ more often in relative frequencies of genetically simple traits than in a trait being present in any individual of one population and always absent in another population. To make things more complex still, the variations of different characters are often independent, or at least not strongly correlated. We have seen (page 83) that people with light and with dark skins may be longheaded and roundheaded, as well as orthognathous and prognathous.

Some populations may be clearly different in gene A but rather similar in gene B, while other populations may be different in B but less so in A. For example, the black-skinned people of Africa and Melanesia (New Guinea and adjacent islands) have frizzly, woolly, or "peppercorn" hair; however, some people in southern India and Ceylon are as dark as anybody in Africa or New Guinea, but their hair is wavy or curly or even straight, as among Europeans. Shall one, then, classify according to skin colors, or hair, or blood groups?

Faced with this difficulty, some authors have resolved to cut the Gordian knot—mankind has no races at all! At the risk of multiplying metaphors unduly, this is like throwing out the baby with the bath water! Race classifiers might have indeed preferred to find simple and tidy races, in which every person would conform to the "type" of his race, and would show every one of the characteristics that his race is supposed to possess and no others. Nature has not been obliging enough to make the races conform to this prescription.

Exactly the same difficulties that a student of races encounters in the human species are met with also by zoologists who are working with species of nonhuman animals. Many species of mammals, birds, insects, and other animals are divided into two or several subspecies (a subspecies is a race that has been given a name, usually in Latin). When these subspecies are investigated in detail, it is not uncommonly found that the boundaries between them are blurred by intermediate populations, and that the different characteristics do not always vary together. This has led some zoologists to argue that subspecies do not exist, or at least that they should not be described and given names. One is tempted then to ask a naïve question: Where, then, are races to be found? And if they are nowhere found, what are these visibly different populations of the human species which are usually referred to as races?

No more valid is the argument that, because the word "race" has been so badly misused by various hate mongers that it has become associated in the public mind with unscientific notions and prejudices, we should throw it overboard, and say that mankind has no races, only ethnic groups. This is not convincing. True enough, the meaning of "race" is widely misunderstood; the obligation of the scientist is therefore to set the matter straight, not just to use different words. The scientist who denies the existence of human races may, regardless of how commendable his motives, actually be helping those whose evil influence he wishes to combat.

The question of the "reality" of races and species has been a sort of biological football for a long time. It is really a part of an even older philosophical football—the dispute between the nominalists and the realists. To a nominalist, only individuals (if they) are real; races, species, and all other supposedly biological units are group concepts residing in the minds of those who invent and use them. Classification of organisms is like that of postage stamps, to be arranged as conveniently and effectively as possible in an album. A realist admits that categories of classification would have to be invented if they did not exist in nature. But he finds that some of them do exist, and some are more objective than others. Species, at least in sexual organisms, are not only group concepts, but also biological phenomena, living systems, levels of biological integration, which are there regardless of whether somebody decides to describe and classify them. Mankind is a species and not an abstraction. Races are less rigidly integrated systems than species, and of course less so than individuals. However, in sexually reproducing species, including man, there are distinguishable populations which are breeding communities within which matings occur more frequently than between them. They do represent tangible biological phenomena. They are facts of life.

A Possible Race Classification

The races of the human species are not clear-cut and not discrete because the race boundaries are blurred by the more or less slow but long-sustained gene exchange. The number of races that should be recognized is arbitrary, in the sense that it is a matter of convention and convenience whether one should give names to only a few "major" or also to a larger number of "minor" races. An anthropologist who maintains that there are exactly five, or fifteen, or fifty, or any other fixed number of races is nurturing illusions. On the other hand, there need be nothing arbitrary about race differences; human populations are racially distinct if they differ in the frequencies of some genes, and not distinct if they do not so differ. The presence of race differences can be ascertained, and if they are present, their magnitude can be measured.

S. M. Garn, a modern American anthropologist who is fully aware of the shifting and relative nature of racial subdivisions, has proposed the following ninefold race classification: (1) American Indian—the descendants of the pre-Columbian inhabitants of North and South America, (2) Polynesian—the Pacific Ocean islanders ranging from New Zealand to Hawaii and Easter Island, but excluding the islands occupied by the following two races, (3) Micronesian—the Pacific islands north of the Equator, from Palau and Guam to the Marshall and Gilbert island groups, (4) Melanesian-Papuan—the islands from New Guinea to Fiji, (5) Australian—the Aboriginal populations of the Australian continent, (6) Asiatic—numerically the largest of human races, living from Indonesia, the Philippines, and Japan westward to Tibet, central Asia, Mongolia, Siberia, and arctic America (Eskimos), (7) Indian—many and diverse populations of the Indian subcontinent and Ceylon, (8) European—originally the inhabitants of Europe, North Africa, and the Near East, now world-wide, (9) African—Africa south of the Sahara Desert.

These nine races are quite obviously not equivalent numerically; neither are they fully discrete or internally uniform. Realizing this, Garn indicates a possible further subdivision of six of the nine major races into thirty-two local races. We would then have a list of thirty-five human races. It is just as logical not to make the distinction between the major and the minor races, since they are surely not separate categories of classification. This fluidity of race classifications will not surprise or dismay anybody who understands the nature of the biological episode referred to by the word "race."

Race, Intelligence, Personality

The problem that inevitably arises in any discussion of individual and race diversity is how consequential the differences among humans really are. Man's bodily structures do not differentiate him strikingly from other living creatures; it is the psychic, intellectual, or spiritual side of human nature that is truly distinctive of Man. Physical race differences supply only the externally visible marks by which the geographic origin of people, or, rather, of their ancestors, can be identified. The nose shape, skin color, and blood type of people whom we meet are so much less important to us than their dispositions, intelligence, and integrity. It is man's personality that matters most.

The diversity of personalities would seem to be as great as, and surely more telling than, the diversity of skin color and other physical traits. And, though the biological basis of both kinds of diversity is the same in principle, it is nevertheless different enough in its outward manifestations to constitute a genuine problem. This is the perennial nature-nurture problem, the general features of which were reviewed in Chapter 2. As shown there, the confusion and polemics with which the problem was beset for a long time were due, in part, to the fact that the problem was wrongly stated: Which human traits are owing to heredity and which to environment? No trait can, however, arise unless the heredity of the organism makes it possible, and no heredity operates outside of environment. Furthermore, the issue must be investigated and solved separately for each function, trait, or characteristic that comes under consideration. Suppose that one collects good data on the genetic and environmental components of the observed diversity in intelligence quotients, or in the resistance to tuberculosis. This would not tell us anything about the diversity of temperaments or about resistance to cancer.

Even correctly stated, the nature-nurture problem remains, as we have seen, a formidable one. Dogmatic statements abound on both the hereditarian and the environmentalist side of the controversy, and they usually say much about their authors but not much about the subject at issue. Some partisans of human equality got themselves in the untenable position of arguing that mankind is genetically uniform with respect to intelligence, ability, and other psychic traits. Actually it is, I think, fair to say that whenever any variable trait in man was at all adequately studied genetically, evidence was found of at least some, though perhaps slight, contribution by genetic differences. Being equal has to be compatible with being different, and different in characteristics that are relevant to the specifically human estate, not alone in "skin-deep" traits like skin color.

The current civil rights movement in the United States has elicited a rash of pamphlets that pretend to prove, very "scientifically" of course, that races cannot be equal because they allegedly differ in average intelligence, as measured by the I.Q., in average brain size, and so on.

There is no reason whatever to believe that intelligence or mental capacity is simply proportional to skull capacity. In the first place, brain size is correlated with body size. An elephant's brain is much bigger than any human brain, yet this does not quite mean that elephants are far more brainy than men. Men have larger brains than women, but this fact is nowadays seldom used to argue that women are mentally inferior. As to the races, they do differ in the *average* cranial capacity, but in every race there are individuals with much larger and much smaller brains than the average for any other race. To quote F. S. Hulse: "Some of the big, burly, brachycephalic populations of Siberia, North America and Polynesia have the largest average cranial capacities of any living peoples: 1500 cubic centimeters or more for adult males. Japanese, northern Chinese, and central and northern Europeans have cranial capacities which average well over 1400 cubic centimeters. The smaller peoples living in warmer areas of Europe, Asia, and America, and the African populations in general, have cranial capacities which average between 1300 and 1400 cubic centimeters. Some Pigmy groups and the natives of Australia have average cranial capacities of less than 1300 cubic centimeters. The range in brain size in each of these groups is at least as great as the range in body size."

The total range of cranial capacity in nonpathological human individuals is from about 750 to more than 2,000 cubic centimeters. The great French writer Anatole France had an estimated brain size of about 1,000, and nobody can deny him intelligence. It happens that one of the largest brains, above 2,000, belonged also to a writer, Ivan Turgenev. You may prefer the writings of Turgenev to those of France, or vice versa, but this is hardly related to their respective brain sizes. Turgenev was, however, a big man and France a small one, which fact is a partial explanation of the dimensions of their crania.

As to intelligence, we have seen in the foregoing chapter that properly conducted I.Q. tests do measure a variable trait of some significance for success in schooling, and moreover that this trait is conditioned in part by genetic differences. The key words in the above sentence are "properly conducted." Nobody has yet succeeded in devising "culture-free" tests which would be equally suitable not only for people brought up in countries with different cultures, say for Americans, Japanese, and Australian Aborigines, but even for people brought up in the same country but having different social or linguistic backgrounds. Tests quite reasonable within a certain culture and social class may look ridiculous to people of different cultures or subcultures. This obviously limits their value for predicting scholastic success, and limits even more severely their applicability to an estimation of genetic differences between populations.

During World War I some 1,726,000 men in the armed forces of the United States were given so-called Army Alpha or Beta tests. The results showed unmistakably that the mean score for the Negro draftees was lower than that for the white ones. Those who were delighted to see such a "proof" of Negro racial inferiority were, however, in for a disappointment when the data were published in full. It appeared that the mean score of the Negro draftees from Northern states was higher, not lower, than the mean for the white draftees from Southern states! Subsequent studies, chiefly of school children, showed in addition that among the Negroes in the North the mean I.Q. rose hand in hand with the duration of the residence in that part of the country.

It is evident enough at least that the existing data have not really proved anything concerning the possibility of the existence of genetically conditioned differences in mean intelligence between Negroes and whites in the United States, or for that matter between any races anywhere in the world. It certainly does not follow from this that such differences do not exist. In science, what is not proved today may be proved tomorrow; the only reasonable and honest conclusion is that at present we do not know.

There is, however, one conclusion that can be affirmed safely: whatever differences, if any, exist between the average, or mean, intelligence of different races, these differences are much smaller than the variations within any one "race." In other words, large brains and high I.Q.'s of persons of every racial group are much larger and higher than the averages for their own or any other group. And, conversely, the low variants in every race are much below the average for any race. This is a situation quite analogous to what is known about race differences in such traits as blood groups, and in perfect accord with what is expected in populations that exchange genes. Men must be dealt with on the basis of their humanity, and also on the basis of their qualities and accomplishments as individuals; the practice of treating them according to their race or color is an unintelligent and a nefarious one.

Races of Man and Breeds of Domestic Animals

A pseudo-biological fallacy, dangerous because it is superficially so plausible, alleges that the differences in psychic traits among human individuals and races must be genetically fixed to about the same extent as they are among races or breeds of domestic animals. Anybody who has had any experience with different breeds of dogs, or horses, or cattle knows how different they are in behavior, temperament, disposition, intelligence, trainability, and so on. And although one can to some extent change these characteristics by training and drill, there is no doubt that differences are largely genetic. Hence, so the argument runs, it is sheer obstinacy to doubt that the different behavior of human breeds, of races, is likewise genetic.

A "breed" is, indeed, biologically a situation roughly comparable to a race or a subspecies. Breeds are populations differing in frequencies of some genes. Gene exchange between breeds, for example between different dog breeds, is prevented by regulation of their reproduction by their human masters; the gene exchange between subspecies of wild animals is limited by their living in different geographic territories, and the gene exchange between human races partly by geographic but mostly by cultural factors.

The analogy between the psychological or behavioral differences of domestic animal breeds and of human races is, however, misleading. It overlooks a dissimilarity of critical importance. The behavior of a breed of horses or of dogs is always a part of the complex of characteristics that are deliberately selected by the breeders to fit the animal for its intended use. A hunting dog with the temperament of a Pekingese, a great Dane behaving like a fox terrier, a draft horse as high-strung as a race horse or vice versa, all these monstrosities would be worthless or even dangerous to their human masters. Man has seen to it that in his domestic animals the genes that stabilize the desirable behavior traits are fixed, and that the genes that predispose to variable or undesirable behavior are eliminated.

The ancestor of the domestic dog was the wolf. The behavior of wolves is certainly different from that of any domestic breed, and the difference is doubtless largely genetic (although wolf puppies, if brought up away from their parents, may, for a time and with care, be treated as household pets). Although the domestication of the wolf is a matter of great antiquity, it is possible to envisage how the transformation of the genetic basis of behavior from that of the wolf to that of the domestic dog took place. The instrumentality was doubtless selection. The wild, intractable, untamable, vicious, unfriendly, unreliable animals ran away or were done to death; the ones that served the purposes of or amused their masters were left to live and to reproduce. It was then discovered that dogs can serve many purposes—as hunting companions, guards, and, finally, as pets. This was the reason for the divergence of the different breeds. The dog breeds are obviously, and strikingly, more different in appearance, and in behavior, than are human races. Nevertheless, they are members of the same species, the gene exchange between them taking place, either directly or via the remarkably variable breed called the mongrel, whenever opportunity arises owing to a relaxation of the vigilance of human masters. The scientific name of the species of domestic dog is *Canis familiaris,* and of the wolf *Canis lupus.* It would be more correct to give them the same species name, since biologically the domestic and the wild dogs are conspecific.

Fixity and predictability of behavior in a domestic animal being useful to human masters, the selection was directed to this end. What is biologically as well as sociologically requisite in man is the exact opposite—to be able to learn whatever mode of behavior fits a job to be done, the mores of the group of which one happens to be a member, conduct befitting circumstances and opportunities. Man's paramount adaptive trait is his educability. The "educability," as this word is used here, is much broader than an ability to get good grades and to graduate safely from high school or college; in most general terms, it is the ability to adjust one's behavior to circumstances in the light of experience. We learn to live and live to learn. The biological evolution of mankind has accordingly so shaped the human genes that educability is a universal property of all "normal," that is, nonpathological, individuals. An individual lacking educability would be a misfit in any society; in fact, he would hardly be human. Educability is a diagnostic character of mankind as a species, not of only some of its races.

This universality is no accident either. In all cultures, primitive or advanced, the vital ability is, and always was, to be able to learn whatever is necessary to become a competent member of a group or a society. In advanced civilizations, the variety of functions has grown so enormously that learning came to occupy a considerable fraction of the life span. Even where, as in India, the society was splintered for centuries into castes specialized for different occupations, the ability to learn new professions or trades has been preserved.

How and why, it may be asked, can the genes make some

traits rigidly fixed and others environmentally plastic? Here one must be reminded of some fundamental facts of genetics. It has been stressed in the foregoing chapter that the genes determine not traits or characters, but the ways in which the organism responds to the environment. One does not inherit skin color or intelligence, only genes that make the development of a certain color and intelligence possible. To state the same thing with a slightly different emphasis, the gene complement determines the path the development of a person will take, given the sequence of the environments that this person encounters in the process of living. Any developmental process, whether physiological or psychological, can be influenced or modified by genetic as well as by environmental variables.

The genetic endowment of a living species is shaped in the process of organic evolution of which this species is a product. Whether the genes will make a given trait rigidly fixed or responsive to environmental influences will be decided by what is more advantageous to the species in its adaptation to its environments. Although the mode of inheritance of physical and psychic traits in man is fundamentally the same, their developmental plasticity, the ability to respond to modifying influences of the environment, is different. There is no known way to alter the blood group with which a person is born; it is however possible to modify one's skin color, making it somewhat darker or lighter by sun tanning or by lack of sun exposure; the development of personality traits, for its part, is very much dependent on the family and social environments in which an individual is brought up and lives.

The great environmental plasticity of psychic traits in man is no biological accident. It is an important, even crucial, evolutionary adaptation, which distinguishes man from other creatures, including those nearest to him in the zoological system. It is by brain, not by brawn, that man controls his environment. Mankind's singular, and singularly powerful, adaptive instrument is culture. Culture is not inherited through genes; it is acquired by learning from other human beings. The ability to learn, and thus to acquire a culture and to become a member of a society, is, however, given by the genetic endowment that is mankind's distinctive biological attribute. In a sense, human genes have surrendered their primacy in human evolution to an entirely new, nonbiological or superorganic agent, culture. However, it should not be forgotten that this agent is entirely dependent on the human genotype; human culture is not possible without human genes.

In Praise of Diversity

Champions of human equality have traditionally been environmentalists, conspicuously distrustful of genetic determinisms. Historically, their attitude has been useful in counterbalancing the influence of those racist hereditarians who try to justify the denial of equality of opportunity to people on the pretext that they allegedly are biologically inferior. The partisans of equality went, however, too far in their protest. They simply failed to understand that to be equal is not the same thing as to be alike. Equality, it cannot be repeated too often, is an ethical and sociological, not a biological, ideal. And what is more, in a society composed of genetically identical individuals, equality would be meaningless; individuals would have to be assigned to different occupations by drawing lots or in some other arbitrary manner. The ideal of equality of opportunity is precious because it holds out a hope that persons and groups diverse in their endowments may enjoy a feeling of belonging and of partnership, and may work for the common good in whatever capacity without loss of their human dignity.

Genetic diversity, is, therefore, a blessing, not a curse. Any society, and particularly any civilized society, has a multitude of diverse vocations and callings to be filled, and new ones are constantly emerging. Human genetically secured educability enables most individuals of all races to be trained for most occupations. This is certainly the basic and fundamental adaptive quality of all mankind, yet this is in no way incompatible with a genetically conditioned diversity of preferences and special abilities within each race. Music is an obnoxious noise to some, ecstatic pleasure to others. Some have a bodily frame that can be trained for championship wrestling, or running, or sprinting, or weight lifting. Some can develop phenomenal abilities for chess playing, or painting, or composing poetry.

Can anybody develop a skill in any of these occupations if he makes sufficient effort? Possibly many people could, to some extent. The point is, however, that what comes easily to some requires great exertion from others, and even then the accomplishment is mediocre at best. The willingness to strive derives, however, at least in part, from a feeling that the labor is rewarded by the thrill of accomplishment or in some other way. There is little stimulus to exert oneself if the results of the exertions are likely to be pitifully small. John W. Gardner has described the situation perfectly in the following words: "All too many lack the qualities of mind or spirit which would allow them to conceive excellence as a good, or to achieve it if they conceive it. But many more can achieve it than now do. Many, many more can *try* to achieve it than now do. *And the society is bettered not only by those who achieve it but by those who are trying.*" (Author's emphasis)

The sentimentalism of the equalitarians and the selfishness of the racists are equally purblind in the light of biology. Some people believe that there is something unfair and "undemocratic" in giving to gifted children an education different from the average, and even in treating the average differently from the retarded ones. I hope it is not contrary to charity to say that this belief is contrary to reason. The famous motto of Marxian socialism is "from each according to his ability"; it behooves democracy to accord no less recognition to the diversity of human individualities. Equality of opportunity is a practical recognition and acceptance of the diversity of human natures. It is neither fair nor rational to deny to any human being an opportunity for self-fulfillment.

An opportunity to achieve the highest intellectual and spiritual development of which a person is capable should be available regardless of race, social origin, or economic status. The white supremacists and ultraconservatives of various sorts would deny this opportunity to a majority of mankind, on the pretext that only an elite (of which they invariably consider themselves to be members) is capable of profiting from it. Racist propaganda in the United States and in some other countries is directed particularly toward withholding equality of opportunity from several million people belonging to the Negro caste, who are alleged to be incompetent to turn it to account. It is sad to see persons otherwise decent and reasonable succumb to so transparent a misconception. In the first place, both ethics and reason demand that human beings be given a chance to show their capacities before they are rated competent or incompetent. Moreover, there are all degrees and many different kinds of competence and incompetence. And finally, different degrees of competence exist in every human population. It is evil to deny the opportunity of self-fulfillment to a minority. With any race and any group of people, there will be some who will fall short of what is expected of them and what they expect of themselves. This involves pain and disappointment. It is debatable whether the pain and disappointment are easier to accept if they are felt to be owing to one's own shortcomings than to an injustice inflicted by others. The former is preferable to the society. It is surely intolerable to be told that one is not entitled even to try to climb a height because of the color of one's skin or a lack of social status in one's ancestors.

Equality of opportunity is not an end in itself, but a means to an end. This can only be the self-actualization of human individuals and the fullest possible realization of their socially valuable capacities and potentialities. Individuals and groups will arrange their lives differently, in accordance with their diverse notions of what form of happiness they wish to pursue. Their contributions to mankind's store of achievements will be different in kind and different in magnitude. The point is, however, that everybody should be able to contribute up to the limit of his ability.

To deny equal opportunity to persons and to groups of persons leads to wastage of talent, ability, and aptitude. Equality of opportunity would mean a more nearly full utilization of these human qualities, besides being in accord with the basic ethic of humanity.

[IV]

Genetic Load and Radiation Hazard

Nature, and particularly living nature, is a realm of great beauty. Not all scientists have chosen science as their life work because of Nature's aesthetic appeal, but a scientist must be obtuse indeed to overlook the beauty entirely. And speaking of beauty, I do not refer only, or even mainly, to such obviously magnificent things as dazzling flowers, butterflies, and birds of paradise. More subtle, but also more lasting for those who know enough to see them, are two beautiful aspects of life: its unity and its diversity.

All living creatures, from the lowest to the highest, are astonishingly similar in fundamentals. Life occurs everywhere in discrete parcels—individuals. Life produces more life by converting a part of its environment, food in the broadest use, into living substance. Though endlessly varying in details, there are only a limited number of methods of reproduction. By far the most widespread is sexual reproduction. Sex in animals and in plants, in simple and in complex organisms, rests on the same twin mechanisms of fertilization and chromosome reduction, the latter usually taking the form of meiosis (see Chapter II). Wherever sex is found, the inheritance is according to the rules discovered by Mendel. The hereditary materials are differentiated into genes. In accordance with the theory outlined in Chapter I, the genes are essentially different concatenations of the four "letters" of the genetic "alphabet," A, T, C, and G.

On the other hand, the diversity of life is immense. It has already been mentioned that there are no fewer than two million species now living on earth, and there may be twice that many. Excepting the frozen wastes of the Arctic and the Antarctic and the permanent snows of the high mountains, where life is relatively scarce, there are usually thousands of species living in the same general neighborhood. A number of years ago, T. M. Pires, G. A. Black, and I counted as many as 179 species of trees growing in an area of about fourteen acres in an equatorial rain forest not far from Belém, Brazil. Some thousands of species of insects can be collected in a state like New York, or Minnesota, or California, and by no means all of the species found in these states are the same. As a general rule, the diversity of species grows from the cold to temperate to tropical countries.

Evolution

Several scientists debated the idea of evolution before Darwin, notably the great French biologist Lamarck in 1809. It was, however, the genius of Darwin that made the idea of evolution the pivotal generalization of biology. The year 1859, which saw the publication of Darwin's great book *On the Origin of Species,* is one of the turning points not in the history of biology alone, but in the intellectual history of mankind. It gave man a new insight into his own nature, and into that of the world in which he lives.

Nothing makes sense in biology except in the light of evolution. The diversity of living beings is a response of living matter to the diversity of the environments on earth. If there existed only one uniform environment on our planet, then a single form of life might have been sufficient to exploit it. In reality, the environments are varied, and there are countless different ways of making a living in many of them. No organism is a Jack-of-all-trades that can exploit all the opportunities. There are instead many different organisms that have mastered different opportunities. The main reason why different organisms are nevertheless basically similar is that they have descended from common ancestors. The structure of man's body and, even more, the physiological processes in it are in many ways similar to those in other living beings, because man is kin to everything else that lives.

Evolution is change. Mankind and all other biological species are products of a historical development extending back to the dawn of life. Our ancestors were not men; they were more and more different from ourselves as one goes down deeper and deeper into the past. The same holds true for all other now-existing forms of life—all are descended from ancestors more or less unlike themselves. Moreover, the evolution has been, not always and not in all lines of descent, but on the whole, progressive. We do not know what primordial life was like; the origin of life may have been a unique event or it may have occurred repeatedly. It is safe to say that by and large organisms evolved from less complex to more complex forms. Man is a newcomer on earth; if the time during which life of any kind is estimated to have existed (about two billion years) be likened to a day, then the million, or at most two million, years since the appearance of manlike creatures amounts to only about one minute.

Mutation

Darwin, and biologists since Darwin, have striven to discover the mechanisms that bring evolution about.

Evolution is, in a sense, the converse of heredity. Heredity tends to make the progeny like their parents; on the molecular level, the really remarkable property of that extraordinary substance DNA is that its structure permits precise replication of the arrangement of the "letters" of the "genetic alphabet" and thus ensures the continuity of the gene from generation to generation. Heredity is a conservative force; evolutionary innovation demands that heredity be occasionally thwarted. This is what takes place when there occurs a mutation.

The study of mutations in *Drosophila melanogaster,* a species of fly variously dubbed vinegar fly, pomace fly, or fruit fly, was, as stated above (Chapter I), initiated in 1909 by T. H. Morgan, then at Columbia University, New York. He raised in laboratory cultures and examined carefully many thousands of individuals in the progenies of Drosophila flies. As expected, most of these individuals were "normal" or "wild-type," that is, they resembled closely their progenitors living outside the laboratories. However, once in a while Morgan found flies, usually single individuals among masses of wild-type culture mates, which differed in some trait or traits. In the progenies of these mutant individuals, the mutant traits were inherited according to Mendel's laws. True-breeding strains of many mutants were obtained; descendants of some of these strains, hundreds of generations removed from the original mutants, are still maintained in many laboratories throughout the world.

Examples of these classical Drosophila mutants are shown in Figure 15. There are mutant flies with cut, rudimentary, vestigial, and curly wings, bar eyes, forked bristles, and so on. Many mutants are known with body colors darker and others lighter than in normal flies, with eyes brighter and duller than the normal red, with white eyes, with various kinds of altered or absent bristles. Many mutants are known that are not as easily represented in pictures as those in Figure 15. Among these are numerous

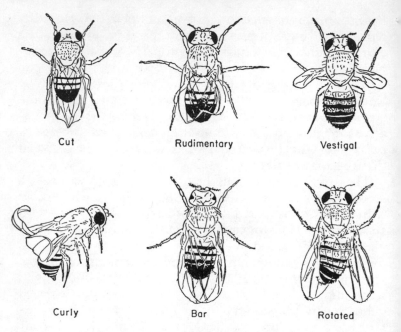

Cut   Rudimentary   Vestigal

Curly   Bar   Rotated

Figure 15. Some mutants in the fly *Drosophila melanogaster,* showing changes in the wings, eyes, or the abdomen.

lethal or semilethal mutants which kill all or a part of their carriers before they attain the adult stage of development, that is, in the egg or larval or pupal stages. These mutants may be said to produce fatal hereditary diseases in the flies, just as there are many hereditary diseases in man. True-breeding strains of these death-dealing mutants obviously cannot be obtained; lethal and semilethal mutants often behave, however, as Mendelian genes that are recessive to the normal, or healthy, condition, and they can be maintained in laboratory cultures by breeding in each generation normal-appearing (heterozygous) carriers.

Mutations have been observed in many organisms besides Drosophila. In recent years, bacteria, viruses, and other microorganisms have become the most extensively used materials for mutations studies. The reason for using them for such studies is simple—Drosophila flies can be bred by the thousand or, at the most, by the million, while a single culture of bacteria may contain billions of individuals. This makes even very rare mutations detectable if proper techniques are used. The kind of mutations most often studied in microorganisms are biochemical ones. Using methods originally developed by G. W. Beadle and E. L. Tatum, one starts the experiment with a strain of a given microorganism that can grow successfully in a test tube or on an agar plate with a certain "minimal" medium, containing chemical substances indispensable for the growth of the organism in question. Many mutants that arise make the organism unable to grow on the minimal medium, since they require certain additional substances in the food which the original strain can get along without. When the missing substance is identified and added to the minimal medium, the mutant may grow quite well. The study of such biochemical mutants proved to be of outstanding interest not only to genetics, but also to biochemistry and to chemical physiology.

Mutations in Man

Even though man is not an easy species in which to study mutations, research on human mutations has made a not inconsiderable progress. As an example of the methods used in this research, consider a rather common form of dwarfism known as achondroplasia (or chondrodystrophy). Achondroplastic dwarfs have heads and bodies of about normal size, but their extremities, arms and legs, are very short. This condition is owing to a dominant Mendelian gene. Now, some achondroplasts are children of parents at least one of whom is also an achondroplast. These children have probably inherited their genes for achondroplasia from their parents. Some achondroplasts are, however, born to parents neither of whom has this condition. It is reasonable to conclude that they carry an achondroplasia gene newly arisen by mutation. Knowing how many such mutants and how many normal nonachondroplastic children are born in a given state or country during a certain period, one can estimate how frequent is the mutation giving rise to achondroplasia. E. T. Mørch collected such data in the population of Denmark, and concluded that approximately four out of every 100,000, or a fraction of 0.00004, of the sex cells produced by normal, nonachondroplastic, persons contain a newly arisen mutant gene for achondroplasia. Data of similar nature exist for about a dozen human genes; rough estimates of the mutation frequencies, all of them subject to correction by more extensive studies, are of the order of one per 10,000 to one per 100,000 normal sex cells.

Mutation will appear to be either a rare or a common occurrence depending on how you look at it. The chance 4:100,000 of a mutational origin of achondroplasia is low enough so that prospective parents, neither of whom is an achondroplast, need not worry about giving birth to an achondroplastic child. The gene that changes normal to achondroplastic growth in man is, however, only one of many human genes. How many genes man has, or, for that matter, how many genes a Drosophila fly has, is not known; very imprecise estimates range from 10,000 per sex cell upward. If all genes undergo mutation with average frequencies about like that of achondroplasia, the combined incidence of all mutations would be quite substantial. If, let us suppose, man has at least 20,000 genes (10,000 from his mother and an equal number from his father), the chances become 0.00004 x 20,000, or 0.8. It would seem then that 80 per cent of the individuals born contain in their genetic endowments a mutant gene they have not inherited from their parents. This may be an overestimate, because two or more new mutants may by coincidence be in the same person; on the other hand, 10,000 genes per sex cell is probably an underestimate. Even taking the low estimate of 10,000 genes and 1:100,000 as the mutation rate per gene, the calculation gives about 20 per cent, or about one in five individuals born, as the number of carriers of newly arisen mutant genes. It is clear, then, that mutation is not at all a rare phenomenon.

Kinds of Mutation and Their Causes

To date, it has not been possible to validate the above estimates of the frequency of mutations by direct observation, either in man or in any other organism. Let us make it very clear what makes such validation so difficult. Mutations from normal growth to achondroplastic dwarfism in man, or from the normal red to the white eye color in Drosophila, cause visible changes in their carriers which are too obvious to be overlooked. Not all mutations lead, however, to such easily noticeable changes. The Drosophila mutants shown in Figure 15, or pictured in most treatises and textbooks of biology, are a selected group, selected precisely because they differ from normal or wild-type flies so clearly that an observer, even a beginning student, will have no difficulty recognizing them. Even an inexperienced geneticist working with Drosophila knows, however, that many, in fact most, mutations that arise cause changes that are so slight they can be overlooked unless the observer searches carefully, or unless special and complicated techniques are used for their detection. Many mutants do not change the appearance of the fly at all, and cause, instead, subtle changes in its physiological traits, such as viability, fecundity, longevity, behavior, and so on. Nobody has as yet succeeded in inventing a technique to detect all mutations that arise in Drosophila or anywhere else.

Mutations that produce changes too obvious to be overlooked, and those with small and subtle effects, sometimes referred to as polygene mutations, are not two separate categories. The effects of mutations are best described as forming a spectrum, from drastic changes, which cause death of the embryo or lethal hereditary diseases, to changes so slight that they are hard to detect. Most, though not all, mutations are alterations of the genetic messages coded in the DNA of the chromosomes. Some are changes of a rather cruder sort, due to reduplication, deletion, or repatterning of chromosome sections or of whole chromosomes. An example of a mutation of this latter sort in man is the condition known as Down's syndrome (also, misleadingly, called mongolism, or mongolian idiocy, since it has nothing to do with the characteristics of the Mongolian race).

Individuals with this condition have a characteristic cast of facial features and are greatly retarded in mental as well as physical development. The condition is unfortunately not rare; since about two children per 1,000 develop Down's syndrome, some 8,000 out of the approximately four million babies born annually in the United States are likely to be affected. For a long time Down's syndrome was a kind of genetic puzzle; its incidence is somehow related to the age of the mother, close to 40 per cent of the affected children being born to mothers aged forty or older. Some authorities have even argued that Down's syndrome was not genetic at all. Then, in 1959, J. Lejeune, M. Gautier, and R. Turpin in France discovered that three boys with Down's syndrome each had forty-seven, instead of the usual forty-six chromosomes in their body cells. It was later found that the extra chromosome is No. 21 of the set of twenty-three, one of the smallest chromosomes in the human chromosome complement. An individual with Down's syndrome has this chromosome in triplicate, instead of in duplicate, as normal. The origin of this condition is most likely that the pair of the No. 21 chromosomes occasionally fail to disjoin at meiosis, so that egg cells with two and with no No. 21 chromosomes are formed. Fertilized by normal spermatozoa with a single No. 21, these egg cells will give individuals with forty-seven (triple No. 21, Down's syndrome) and with forty-five chromosomes (presumed inviable).

Reference has been made (page 20) to the occasional nondisjunction of the sex chromosomes in Drosophila flies, which gave the opportunity to C. B. Bridges to carry out his classic study on the relations between the chromosomes, genes, and sex. Similar failures of disjunction at meiosis are now known in man also. In recent years, cases have been discovered of persons having forty-five chromosomes, including one X-chromosome and no Y-chromosome, and also with forty-seven and forty-eight chromosomes, including two X's plus a Y-chromosome, three and even four X-chromosomes, three X's plus a Y-chromosome, and still others. Interestingly enough, the study of these cases showed that the determination of sex in man deviates considerably from the Drosophila model. An XXY individual in Drosophila is a quite normal and fertile female; in man, the XXY condition gives the so-called Klinefelter syndrome—sexually and usually also mentally underdeveloped boys with very small testes. The single X- and no Y-chromosome individuals in Drosophila are normal-appearing but sterile males, while in man they show Turner's syndrome—infantile development of mammary glands and other female sexual traits, with ovaries very small or absent. The XXX individuals in Drosophila are sterile and poorly viable "superfemales"; in man, the individuals with the triple-, and even quadruple-X condition are normal, though often mentally retarded, women. It appears, then, that in man it is the presence of the Y-chromosome that makes an individual a male, while the X-chromosome carries genes for femaleness.

A great majority of mutations cause, however, no changes in the chromosomes visible under even the best microscopes. They are owing to chemical alterations within the genes, presumably to additions, deletions, or rearrangements of the nucleotides, the "letters" of the "genetic alphabet." What is the cause of such alterations? This is hardly a satisfactory explanation, but one can say that mutations are owing to incorrect copying, to occasional mistakes in the generally so remarkably accurate process of replication of the sequence of genetic "letters" in the chromosomal DNA, which has to occur every time genes multiply. You may, if you wish, compare mutations to accidental misspellings or misprints which even the most experienced copyists and typesetters make from time to time. Yet these "mistakes" are of tremendous biological significance, since mutations supply the genetic raw materials from which evolutionary changes are constructed.

Are Mutations Mostly Harmful?

Looking at mutations as genetic "mistakes" will be helpful in understanding the otherwise astonishing property of most of them, namely, the fact that mutant genes and chromosomes are usually harmful to the organism that carries them. The examples of mutations given above are really a collection of various defects and hereditary diseases, and such examples can be indefinitely multiplied. The clear-cut mutants of Drosophila, with which so much of the classical research in genetics was done, are almost without exception inferior to wild-type flies in viability, fertility, longevity, and in all these features. This matter deserves careful consideration, and such consideration shows that the harmfulness of most mutants is just what could reasonably be expected. Indeed, the genetic machinery of a living species, its genotype, is exquisitely adjusted to the environment in which this species lives. An accident, a random change, in any delicate mechanism can hardly be expected to improve it. Poking a stick into the machinery of one's watch or one's radio set will seldom make it work better.

And yet mutations can also lead to evolutionary improvements. How is this possible? I have said that the genotype of every species is adapted to the environment in which this species lives. The environment changes, however; the climate of North America or of Europe, for example, is now different from what it was during the Ice Age. Human environments now are not what they were a thousand years ago, or even a generation ago. It is a remarkable fact that organisms are so well adapted to the conditions in which they live and in which their ancestors lived; it is too much to expect that as they are now they will also be adapted to environments this species will encounter in the future. What then is a possible solution?

A gene need not be unconditionally good or bad, useful or harmful, adaptive or unadaptive. If the environment changes, some genes that were favorable in the old environments may become unfavorable, and others may become favorable. This is not merely a theoretical possibility. The genetics of microorganisms has discovered many diagrammatically clear examples of this. In many species of bacteria there occur mutants resistant to some antibiotics, say to penicillin, or to streptomycin, or to a sulfa drug. These mutants arise in bacterial cultures regardless of whether the latter are or are not exposed to the respective antibiotics or drugs. It happens, however, that in the absence of drugs and antibiotics the "resistant" mutants not only have no advantage, but are, in fact, at a disadvantage compared to the ordinary nonresistant variety. The situation changes completely when an antibiotic is introduced. Then the resistant mutants survive and multiply, while the nonresistant forms are destroyed.

Natural Selection

Mutation, then, does not make evolution by itself; the process of mutation supplies only the raw materials for evolution. The raw materials for building a house, the bricks, lumber, and so on, do not in themselves make a livable house; they must be arranged in a certain pattern if a house is to be built. There is, indeed, a natural process that acts like a builder of a house from its raw materials.

Natural selection is the process that builds evolutionary changes from the raw materials supplied by mutation. The great seminal idea of natural selection, though adumbrated by some of Darwin's predecessors, was formulated by Darwin and A. R. Wallace in 1858 and by Darwin in 1859. It developed greatly during the century since Darwin. As we see it at present, natural selection occurs when the carriers of some genotypes contribute more surviving progeny to the succeeding generations in relation to what the carriers of other genotypes contribute. In a bacterial culture exposed to penicillin, the penicillin-resistant mutants reproduce and the nonresistant form is killed off; in a culture without penicillin, the nonresistant bacteria outbreed the resistant ones.

Natural selection has been compared to a builder of a house. This analogy should not be taken too literally; natural selection is a name for an impersonal process of nature; it is not a conscious agent of any sort. It is not like an engineer who does things according to a plan. All it does is to further the perpetuation from generation to generation of genes favorable in the existing environment, and to slow down the transmission of the less favorable genes. It is an agency of the environment, a means whereby the conditions of life exert a directing influence on the evolution of organisms. Herbert Spencer, and Darwin, following him, said that natural selection leads to "the survival of the fittest." As we shall see, the fittest, or simply the fit, is nothing like the superman but simply the carrier of a genetic endowment that leaves the greatest number of surviving descendants.

If the environment in which a population lives remains reasonably constant for a long time, then most of the useful mutants will be established as the adaptive norm, and most or all mutants that arise will be harmful. If the environment changes, some of the mutants may become advantageous, will be perpetuated by natural selection, and may eventually replace the ancestral form. In a constant environment, natural selection is in general a conservative force which favors stability and discriminates against mutants. This important but unspectacular form of selection is called normalizing selection; its existence was realized actually by some of Darwin's predecessors, especially by Edward Blyth. Environmental changes present a challenge to the species, to which this species may respond, by means of natural selection, provided that genetic raw materials are available, by changing its genotype to fit the new environment.

Genetic Load

Normalizing natural selection is constantly and unrelentingly working to remove from a living population the disadvantageous genes. Why, it may be asked, is there so much hereditary ill-health tormenting mankind? The answer may be given under two headings: the occurrence of harmful mutations and the less than perfect efficiency of natural selection.

In every generation numerous mutations, of every possible degree of harmfulness, will arise in the human species; in every generation, the carriers of some of these mutants—persons afflicted with hereditary diseases, malformations, or constitutional weaknesses—will die before they have children, or will remain unmarried, or will produce fewer children than they would have produced if they did not carry the mutant genes in question. Consider the mutation for retinoblastoma, the illness already mentioned (page 68). Before the surgical treatment of retinoblastoma was developed, most of the infants carrying this dominant mutant gene died, and the mutant genes were thus removed from the population. Since, however, new mutants inevitably arose in every generation, new cases of retinoblastoma kept appearing and being eliminated by death. For a dominant lethal gene like retinoblastoma, the population will have twice as many cases of retinoblastoma as there will be functioning sex cells carrying the mutant gene. (There will be twice as many because it takes two sex cells to form an individual, and a mutant gene in either of them will cause retinoblastoma.)

Consider now another dominant mutation, also previously mentioned (page 119), achondroplastic dwarfism. Although mortality among achondroplastic children is higher than among those growing normally, the achondroplastic dwarfs usually survive and enjoy more or less normal health. Nevertheless, Mørch, the author of the classic study on achondroplasia in Denmark, found that the average number of children born to achondroplasts is much smaller than that born to their normal (not achondroplastic) siblings. Their low reproductive rate is owing largely to the fact that most of the dwarfs remain unmarried, but also to difficult childbirth experienced by some achondroplastic mothers. Here, then, we have an instructive situation—the genetic drawback connected with a mutant gene is caused, at least in part, by the notions of handsomeness and sexual attractiveness prevailing in a given society.

Be that as it may, the mutant genes for achondroplasia are transmitted from generation to generation less efficiently than are the genes for normal growth. This is another way of saying that the gene for achondroplasia is discriminated against by natural selection; it is selectively disadvantageous. Natural selection is, however, less efficient in eliminating the mutant form of the gene causing achondroplasia than it is in eliminating retinoblastoma. In every generation the human population will contain achondroplasia genes that arose by mutation in that generation (or, rather, carried in the sex cells that gave rise to it), a certain fraction of such genes which arose a generation ago, a smaller fraction which arose two generations ago, and so on. Or, to put it differently, a certain average number of generations will elapse between the origin by mutation and the elimination by natural selection of the genes for achondroplasia. Meanwhile, the genes for achondroplasia and for other hereditary diseases, abnormalities, defects, and weaknesses carried in a population will constitute the genetic load of that population.

Particularly important as constituents of the genetic load are harmful mutant genes that are recessive to the healthy or normal state. Two rare recessive hereditary diseases, galactosemia and acrodermatitis enteropathica, have been mentioned (pages 68-70), as has been a much more common defect, diabetes mellitus, which many authorities consider to be also recessive to the normal, nondiabetic, state. There are literally hundreds of other variations in man known or suspected to be caused by recessive genes. Now, a recessive gene, although it may produce a dangerous or even lethal disease or a striking abnormality in double dose (in homozygous condition), may not manifest itself at all in single dose (in heterozygous condition). To put it differently, a person of robust health may (and as shown below usually does) carry one or more genes concealed in heterozygous condition that would cause some ill-health or malformation or constitutional weakness if these genes were homozygous.

The harmful recessive genes carried in heterozygous condition constitute the concealed genetic load. The concealed load manifests itself when two persons who are heterozygous carriers of the same harmful recessive gene (a fact of which they are usually quite unaware) marry; about one in four children that they produce is likely to show the defect in homozygous condition. What is important to realize is that, because recessive defects are mostly hidden in heterozygous carriers, the average number of generations that will elapse between the origin by mutation and the elimination by selection is generally much greater for recessive than for dominant defects. The concealed genetic load is vastly greater than the visible, expressed, or manifested genetic load.

The burden of genetic ill-health and abnormality in human populations is very great. The most successful attempt to estimate its magnitude was made by A. C. Stevenson, in Northern Ireland. He found that at least 4 per cent of the infants born carry genetic defects that will cause them to be more or less seriously incapacitated at some time during their lives. This does not include abortions and stillbirths, which occur in some 14 per cent of recordable pregnancies, and some of which are doubtless genetic. Even more important, the figure does not include such common diseases as diabetes and schizophrenia, the aggregate frequency of which is quite large, and in the causation of which genetic factors are involved. Stevenson also estimated that about 26 per cent of the hospital beds in Northern Ireland are occupied by genetically handicapped persons, and that some 6 per cent of consultations with medical practitioners and 8 per cent of those with medical specialists involve such persons. The incidence of clinical schizophrenia is generally about 1 per cent, but in some populations in northern Sweden it is between 2 and 3 per cent. Schizophrenics make up about half of the resident population in mental hospitals; in the United States in 1961, about 800,000 persons were receiving psychiatric care. Blindness, deaf-mutism, and other severe sensory defects afflict about one third of 1 per cent of the population, and many of these defects are also genetically conditioned.

Adaptively Ambivalent Genetic Conditions

Natural selection seems not to be doing its work as effectively as we might wish it would. Well, natural selection is a part of this imperfect world in which we live. Here is a warning against an erroneous notion that has achieved some currency in popular scientific literature, the notion that the heavy genetic load of mankind is the result of civilization, technology, and modern medicine. This is simply not so. Populations of Drosophila flies, natural, wild, and surely unspoiled by civilization or medicine, carry very heavy genetic loads, which can be measured more precisely than those in man.

Flies of several species of Drosophila were collected in their natural habitats and submitted to genetic analysis. The "wild" flies themselves are, with rare exceptions, very uniform in external appearance, except for variation in size, which depends largely on the amount of food consumed and on the temperature prevailing during the larval development. The female flies collected in nature (and usually already inseminated there) were then placed in individual cultures, and their progenies were inbred by mating brothers and sisters for several generations. Mating of close relatives increases the probability of the appearance in the offspring of some individuals homozygous for the genes that were carried in heterozygous condition in the wild ancestors. There are also other, more complex but more exact, genetic techniques for enforcing homozygosis in fly progenies.

What these methods revealed is that about half (more in some, fewer in other species) of the wild flies carry one or more recessive lethal genes, which would kill the animal in double dose; almost always more than one recessive gene that makes the homozygote "subvital," that is, less viable or vigorous than a heterozygote; very often a sterility gene, which in double dose makes either female or male flies unable to leave progeny; and commonly also genes giving various abnormalities in the physiology or in the external appearance of the animal. It is difficult to compare meaningfully the genetic load in organisms as different as a Drosophila fly and man. An ingenious mathematical calculation was devised for this purpose by N. E. Morton, J. F. Crow, and H. J. Muller. A tentative conclusion is that these genetic loads are of the same order of magnitude, and man's is somewhat heavier.

A genetic load is, then, not something novel, a curse recently arisen to plague man. At least all sexually reproducing organisms have carried genetic loads during their whole evolutionary histories. Is it possible that the adaptation to the environment has somehow utilized at least a part of the load for the benefit of the species? The occurrence of some mutation is unavoidable; mutations are mostly accidents in the self-replication of the genes, and accidents will occur. Some of these accidents may happen to be favorable in some environments. Any list of human hereditary diseases contains, however, many afflictions that can hardly be imagined to be doing any good to anybody. And still other genetic variants exhibit a curious ambivalence, that is, they are useful in single dose, in heterozygous condition, and harmful in double dose. Here is an example of such an ambivalence taken from human genetics.

Sickle-cell anemia is a disease found not uncommonly in many populations native of tropical Africa and in some populations of tropical Asia. It is owing to a single Mendelian gene, which changes the chemical composition of the hemoglobin, the pigment of the red blood cells. In fact, sickle-cell hemoglobin differs from the normal in the substitution of a single amino acid in the protein molecule; the mutation that transformed the normal gene into the sickle-cell variant involved a change in probably a single "letter" in the genetic "message." The change of this single "letter" has consequences that are quite dramatic—individuals who receive a sickle-cell gene from both parents, that is, the sickle-cell homozygotes, suffer from severe anemia, and most of them die before adolescence. In the language of genetics, sickle-cell anemia is due to a recessive lethal gene.

In the populations in which the sickle-cell gene is frequent, a certain proportion of the infants born in every generation fail to reach maturity. The high frequencies of such a death-dealing gene were puzzling until A. C. Allison, an English geneticist, showed that persons who carry a single dose of the sickle-cell gene, the heterozygotes, have in some environments an advantage over persons who do not carry this gene at all. The heterozygous carriers of the sickle-cell gene can be recognized by the shape of their red blood cells in certain microscopic preparations. They are not anemic, and are, in fact, relatively more resistant to certain tropical fevers (falciparum malaria) than are persons without sickle-cell genes.

The action of natural selection in human populations that contain the sickle-cell gene is quite interesting. Whether this gene is adaptively favorable or unfavorable evidently depends on the environment. Falciparum malaria was a real scourge in many tropical countries; the mortality from it was severe until the antimalarial drugs, developed particularly during and since World War II, began to control it rather successfully. A tribe of people that included many heterozygotes for the sickle-cell gene had therefore a selective advantage if they lived in a malaria-ridden country. To be sure, this advantage was paid for by the death from sickle-cell anemia of a certain number of homozygotes in every generation. Many of the noncarriers also succumbed, but the population as a whole was not wiped out by the disease. The situation changes if the population moves to a country free of falciparum malaria, or if the malaria is eradicated. The sickle-cell gene then has no known advantage. In fact, there are some indications that the frequency of sickle-cell genes in the Negro population in the United States is decreasing. If so, this is a good example of the dependence of natural selection on the environment.

How great is the fraction of the genetic load in man that is kept up in populations by the action of natural selection is one of the great open problems of modern genetics. It is surely not the entire load; many mutant conditions are probably unconditionally harmful. Others may be favorable, if they exhibit a hybrid vigor in heterozygotes, like the sickle-cell gene in malarial environments. A fact that should not be forgotten or underestimated is that every living species faces always not one uniform environment but a variety of environments; genetic diversity is, then, adaptive, provided that some of the variant genes confer a high fitness in some and others in other environments. The carriers of these genes will, however, suffer, or at least be at a disadvantage, if they happen to be born or placed not in the particular environment that is most favorable for them. There is no rigorous scientific proof for this, but I suspect that some human woe is caused by people taking up occupations other than those for which they are best fitted by their genes.

Genetic Radiation Hazard

Mutations continue to arise in man, as they do in all other organisms, and even as they did since the dawn of time, for otherwise evolution could not have happened. Taking a long-range view, genetic loads are the price that life pays for being able to adapt itself to the diversity and to the changes in the environments by means of evolutionary changes. Such a view is nonsense if one tries to apply it to man. In the first place, the adaptation in man occurs chiefly by cultural rather than by genetic means. Moreover, a majority of mutations are not useful, but deleterious. In man, more mutation means more distress for more people. Mankind would benefit from having the frequency of mutations reduced, and would suffer from having their frequency increased. This does not mean that mankind must forsake all biological evolutionary improvement in the future. Human populations contain an ample supply of genetic variability from which selection could construct new adaptive hereditary endowments. The genetic variability, having arisen, of course, by mutation in the past, is sufficient for any conceivable evolutionary engineering that man may decide to undertake. This would require not more mutation, but more selection of the already existing variants.

Unfortunately, man has not so far learned how to reduce

the frequency of mutations. On the contrary, certain technological inventions have inadvertently increased the mutability. One aspect of this problem has, and quite properly, provoked much public concern in recent years. This is the genetic damage inflicted on mankind by exposure to X rays and other radiations. In 1927, H. J. Muller announced that the frequency of mutations is enhanced in the progeny of Drosophila flies treated with X rays. It is known at present that all high-energy, or penetrating, or ionizing radiations are mutagenic, that is, they increase the frequency of mutation in the progeny of exposed individuals. Mutagenic radiations are X rays, gamma rays of radium and other radioactive elements, including fallout from the testing of nuclear weapons, many radiations generated in atomic piles, in so-called "atom smashers," and so on.

High-energy radiations cause two kinds of damage to living matter—physiological and genetic. Physiological damage consists of radiation burns, radiation sickness, and death, which occur relatively soon after the irradiation, and of various delayed effects, such as malignant growths. Genetic damage includes the mutations induced in the reproductive tissues and transmitted to the progeny. The physiological damage, no matter how grievous, is confined to the exposed generation; the injury dies with the injured persons. The genetic damage may inflict harm on the descendants of the exposed persons, and that for many generations after the exposure. Another difference between physiological and genetic damage is also important. Small doses of radiation produce no physiological damage, since there is always some danger threshold above which but not below which the damage begins. Not so with genetic damage; the numbers of mutations induced is simply proportional to the amount of the radiation administered, and there is no minimal or "safe" dose of radiation below which no injury occurs.

It is accordingly inevitable that no matter how small the

amount of radiation received, for example, from the fallout from testing atomic weapons in the atmosphere, it will induce a certain number of mutations in the population exposed. It is wrong to say that any source of radiation is harmless because the amount of the radiation it produces is small, especially if it is the whole of mankind, three billion persons, that is being exposed. It is ethically indefensible to inflict death or suffering on no matter how small a number of guiltless people.

On the other hand, it should not be forgotten that all life has always been exposed to some radiation, since traces of radioactive elements are present inside all living bodies and in their environment. This practically irreducible radiation "background" was always inducing mutations. Attempts have been made to determine how much man-made sources of radiation have added to this background. This is different in different places, and the added radiation is naturally greatest in technologically advanced countries. In the United States, man-made sources have approximately doubled the radiation exposure. This does not mean that the mutation rates have also doubled, because some mutations, the so-called spontaneous ones, are produced by unknown causes other than radiation. However that may be, thus far the main source of man-made radiations is not fallout, but the X rays administered for diagnostic and curative purposes in medical practice. This fact would, of course, change if mankind went insane and started an unlimited nuclear war.

The situation is obviously too complex to please those who like to see things as either pure white or wholly black. The benefits derived from medical applications of radiation are too great to be renounced, but the radiation administered to patients should be reduced as far as possible, and special precautions should be taken against irradiation of the reproductive organs. There is also another problem, which has not received the attention it deserves, namely, the possibility that some chemical substances may also be mutagenic. Modern technology has filled man's environments, particularly in the so-called "advanced" countries, with a whole host of chemical substances used as medicines, drugs, food preservatives, insecticides, fungicides, or generated as industrial wastes, air pollutants, and so on. Some of these chemicals with which we so cheerfully treat ourselves are known to be mutagenic in lower organisms (bacteria), and it is by no means inconceivable that they will prove to be mutagenic also in higher organisms, including man.

Testing nuclear weapons does inflict some genetic damage on mankind, but this was only one of the factors that was considered by those who decided whether testing was to stop or to continue. Anyway, the popular interest aroused by discussions of genetic radiation damage is all to the good, because this is an integral part of a vastly greater problem, which has received nothing like the attention it merits, namely, the problem of the genetic status and of the evolutionary perspectives of mankind.

[V]

Whither Mankind

Science should be anthropocentric, that is, relevant to man. Basic, fundamental, theoretical science is sometimes defined as an attempt to *understand* the world. Applied, practical science, or technology, is an attempt to *change* the world in accordance with man's will and his desires. It stands to reason that in order to know what changes are to be made in the world and how they can be achieved, and even more in order that the changes made shall be to man's benefit, an understanding of the world is useful, and even indispensable. The relevance to man of basic science must, of course, be interpreted broadly. Knowledge of subatomic particles, of atoms and molecules, of organisms high and low, of mountains and oceans, of planets and suns and galaxies, assists man in his quest to understand himself and his place in the universe.

What is man, where did he come from, and where is he going? It is debatable whether science alone can ever hope to answer these questions fully; however, even the best intellects are powerless to face them in the absence of scientific knowledge. Omar Khayyam expressed this most poignantly some eight and a half centuries ago:

> Into this Universe, and Why not knowing,
> Nor Whence, like Water willy-nilly flowing,
> And out of it, as Wind along the Waste,
> I know not Whither, willy-nilly blowing . . .

Darwin may or may not have been familiar with the great poet of Persia, but he sketched a rough draft of partial answers to some of Omar Khayyam's queries. Biologists have been working on this draft for more than a century since Darwin. There has been notable progress, but a vast amount of work remains to be done. Man is the outcome of a long process of evolutionary development. He is kin to all that lives. He not only has evolved, he is evolving. The direction of his evolution is an unsolved problem.

Another poet, Nietzsche, has dared to suggest a solution: "Man is a rope stretched between the animal and the Superman—a rope over an abyss." This is a fine statement of the direction that the evolution of man *ought* to take. But is mankind really evolving toward some sort of Supermankind? Let us not forget that the Nietzschean "rope" hangs over an abyss. There is no assurance that the passage will be accomplished safely; to many of our contemporaries, the abyss seems mankind's likeliest destination. To mention just one danger, and, at that, probably not the gravest one, atomic energy used wisely would benefit mankind enormously, but if misused it may become the instrument of the suicide of the human species. There is no biological law, or any other law of Nature, guaranteeing either evolutionary progress and betterment or deterioration and downfall, of either the human or of any other species.

Culture

Man is, however, an extraordinary creature. The human species has already moved some distance along the

Nietzschean "rope," away from simple animality. Man, and he alone, possesses the faculties of symbolic thought and of self-awareness. Man can contemplate himself as an object among other objects; as a consequence he can choose to control and to dominate himself as he can control and dominate Nature. Like other living beings, man receives sense impressions from Nature; animals know their surroundings, but man also knows that he knows. Other many-cellular animals also die, but man is the only animal who knows that he will die. The human species and other biological species have evolved and are evolving, but only man has discovered the fact of evolution. Only man could therefore, if he will so choose, refuse to accept the evolutionary direction of blind forces of Nature. He may learn to understand, to control, and to guide his evolution.

The first, basic, fundamental fact about human evolution is that mankind is engaged simultaneously in two kinds of evolutionary development—the biological and the cultural. Human evolution can be understood only as a product of the interaction of these two developments. On the biological side, man is one of the two million or more species now living on earth. He is a primate, a mammal, a vertebrate, a sexually reproducing multicellular animal. His heredity, and hence his biological evolution, is much the same as in other creatures, composed of genes, chromosomes, mutations, sexual recombination, natural selection. Man's biological nature resides in the same wonderful stuff, the deoxyribose nucleic acid, DNA, as the nature of a mouse, a fly, a corn plant, or a microbe.

Inescapably, man's nature is in part biological nature. Man is, however, more than DNA's way of making quantities of DNA of a particular kind. Considered biologically as well as philosophically, man is a most singular product of the evolutionary process. He receives and transmits not one, but two heredities, the biological and the cultural. Man's biological heredity is very much like that of any other organism; it is transmitted solely from parents to their children and to other direct descendants. You cannot give your genes even to your best friends or relatives, unless the latter happen to be your children. Cultural heredity, or simply culture, is transmitted by teaching, imitation, learning, in large part by means of language.

In the technical sense in which this word "culture" is used here, all people, modern and ancient, advanced and primitive, have cultures. A culture is not book learning or good table manners, but something much more inclusive; it is the sum total of habits, beliefs, customs, language, techniques of doing things, in general, of all that people do or think as a result of having been so taught. Culture is an exclusively human possession; in zoological species other than man, only the barest traces of cultural transmission can be found, enough for an evolutionist to be satisfied that elements were present in our prehuman ancestors from which the capacity for culture developed in the course of evolution. Human language is a particularly distinctive attribute of culture and the instrument whereby culture is transmitted from generation to generation. The so-called animal "languages," the cries or songs or noises by which an individual bird or mammal communicates with its fellows, are really very different phenomena from human languages. The words composing the latter are conventional symbols standing for objects, actions, or relationships. Human languages are far more efficient than any of their animal precursors as means of communication, but they involve the capacities of symbolic thought and of abstraction, of which only rudiments are found in animals.

Cultures are not transmitted by genes in the sex cells; there are no genes for the American, or Japanese, or Russian, or Papuan culture. Culture is acquired by every person individually from his parents, siblings, teachers, friends, neighbors, books, radio broadcasts, and so on. Every person must be "enculturated" or "socialized," that is, must be instructed in at least the rudiments of the culture of the society of which this person is to become a member. The most important phase of the socialization is childhood, but in a broad sense the socialization of a human being begins at birth and extends until death. The transmission of culture is, in principle, independent of biological descent. We are the cultural inheritors of Darwin, Beethoven, Newton, Plato, the ancient nameless inventors of agriculture and of fire, most of whom were not our biological ancestors. Mankind's cultures, like its genes, have evolved and are evolving.

There is much confusion concerning the relationship between genes and cultures. At one extreme, there are the racists who believe that culture is a matter of race, that the cultural differences between peoples living in different parts of the world are reflections of their genetic differences, and that the history of culture, its inception, progress, or dissolution, is rigidly determined by the changes in the genes of the carriers of that culture. This extreme is refuted rather easily. Cultural changes often proceed much faster than genetic changes in human populations could conceivably happen. One does not have to be very old to have witnessed cultural changes. Our generation and those of our parents and of our grandparents have witnessed prodigious amounts of changes that were cultural and could not be genetic. Millions of workers who now handle complicated machines are sons and grandsons of peasants and farmers who knew only how to till the soil. Surely, the change did not have to wait for gene mutations to make engineers out of farmers.

The extreme opposite of biological racism is the belief that, as far as cultures and their changes are concerned, all people are genetically so completely identical that their genes may just as well be left out of consideration. Adherents of this belief are many, especially among social scientists. It can be understood and perhaps justified only as a reaction against the absurdities of biological racism, which are responsible for so much suffering and evil. But the reaction and protest have gone too far. To be sure, all human beings who are not congenital idiots can acquire at least rudiments not merely of a culture, but of any culture. Most of us use a fork and a spoon instead of chopsticks because we were taught to use them, not because our genes are different from those of the inhabitants of China and Japan. To repeat again, there are no genes for Chinese, or American, or Hottentot culture or language. However, the cultural capacity of the human species did not appear suddenly in some remote ancestor of ours; on the contrary, it must have evolved gradually. Nor is this capacity a constant; it varies from time to time, and from individual to individual. Human genes enable man more or less easily to acquire a culture, but, contrary to what racists think, the genes do not determine what culture he will acquire, just as genes make man able to speak but do not determine what he will say. The maintenance and development of culture is possible only so long as the genetic basis of culture is maintained or improved.

The Rise of Mankind

In *The Descent of Man*, published first in 1871, Darwin argued that man and the now-living anthropoid apes (chimpanzee, gorilla, orangutan, and the gibbons) arose from common ancestors which lived in some remote past. Man, apes, and monkeys had common ancestors which existed in a past probably even more remote. The challenging task to Darwin's followers was to find the fossil remains of these common ancestors, often referred to, especially in popular writings, as the "missing links." Efforts in this direction have met with remarkable success; many links are no longer "missing." Fossil bones of many creatures have been found in several different parts of the African continent, in southern Asia, and even in Europe, which may have belonged to our ancestors, or at least to their collateral relatives.

Discoveries, particularly of the last twenty to thirty

years, make it increasingly more probable that some of the most important evolutionary steps leading toward the emergence of man were taken in Africa, from whence the species ancestral to mankind spread to Asia and to Europe; man has eventually colonized the New World, Australia, and Oceania, and become world-wide in geographic distribution. This does not mean that we now know our ancestry in all detail—many gaps in the record remain to be filled—but the rate of discovery is now so high that they are being filled rapidly. This is not the place to describe the fascinating story of the hunt for the fossil remains of our ancestors and relatives. The problem to be considered is, rather, what caused the ancestors of the human species to evolve the genetic endowment that made culture possible, and thus to embark on the evolutionary adventure that is taking mankind farther and farther away from its animal ancestors.

Darwin thought that man's distinctive features and faculties arose in evolution through natural selection. All that we have learned since Darwin bears him out. The implications of this theory are interesting and should be realized clearly. Natural selection is the factor that translates the challenges of the environment into genetic modifications that make the organism better adapted to live in that environment. The selection of mutants resistant to an antibiotic may transform a culture of bacteria consisting mostly of variants sensitive to that antibiotic into a resistant variety (see page 126). To put it differently, natural selection makes the organism able to live in a new environment, or makes it more successful in its old environment. How does this apply to the problem of man's origin? One may feel optimistic or pessimistic about man's future, but there is no question at all that thus far the human species has been an immense success biologically. Two million years ago, our ancestors were rare and inconspicuous animals living apparently somewhere in Africa; now man is a true cosmopolitan, living all over the world.

He has learned to exploit sources of energy, inorganic and organic, not available to any other creature, and has become adapted to live in all climes.

What is most remarkable of all is that, while all other organisms become masters of their environments by changing their genes, man does so mostly by changing his culture, which he acquires by learning and transmits by teaching. Indeed, many animals have become adapted to living in cold climates by growing warm fur or by becoming dormant when the weather is cold; man has conquered cold by building fires and by wearing warm garments. Adaptation by culture is enormously more rapid and efficient than genetic adaptation; a new thought or a new invention made by one man can become a part of the patrimony of all mankind in a relatively short time. Let us not forget, however, that it is the human genotype that enabled man to invent fire and clothing. Genetic and cultural adaptations are not alternative or mutually exclusive; they are mutually reinforcing. Human genes and human culture are connected by what is known as a circular feedback relationship; in other words, human genes stimulate the development of culture, and the development of culture stimulates genetic changes which facilitate further developments of culture. To say that natural selection has built man's culture is a misleading oversimplification; natural selection has, however, built the genetic endowment that made culture possible.

The analogy between the action of natural selection that led to the emergence of man and that acting to select varieties of bacteria resistant to antibiotics should not be pushed too far either. In bacteria growing on nutrient media that contain penicillin or other antibiotics, the mutants resistant to these antibiotics are perpetuated and the nonresistant forms are eliminated. In the absence of penicillin, the mutants are at a disadvantage, and nonresistant bacteria multiply more rapidly. The prehuman animal was not transformed one fine day into man by a single lucky mutation. The process was vastly more slow and complex, probably thousands of genes undergoing changes, many genes going through several consecutive changes. The selection for penicillin resistance in bacteria is a good model of the elementary component parts, not of the whole evolution of man. The changes in the genes of our ancestors, or at any rate a majority of these changes, happened because they enabled their possessors to outbreed the unchanged forms in the environments in which our ancestors lived at a given time. This should be thought through very carefully, especially because an objection, at first sight serious, has been raised against the theory I have been presenting.

Chance or Design?

The organism of man, or for that matter of any other living being, is a beautifully contrived system of many parts which must all be there together for the organism to function properly, or indeed to remain alive at all. Consider not even the whole organism, but some complex organ, for example, the human eye. It consists of numerous but perfectly dovetailing parts—the transparent cornea, a lens adjustable for focusing at near and distant objects, the vitreous humor, the retina with its rods and cones each supplied with nerve endings, the iris functioning as a regulating diaphragm, a complicated blood supply, a system of muscles, and others. The absence or misformation of any one of these parts makes the eye malfunction or be altogether blind. Can one imagine that so complicated and so nearly perfect a system arose by the compounding of thousands of lucky mutants, mutants that were in the first place accidents or mistakes in the gene replication? Is this not too much for natural selection to accomplish?

This, at first sight formidable, difficulty of any theory of evolution stressing the guiding role of natural selection was fully realized by Darwin himself; in a letter to one of his American correspondents, Asa Grey, Darwin wrote: "The eye to this day gives me a cold shudder." And one of Darwin's critics invented a "monkey analogy" to illustrate the utter improbability of chance mutations being selected together to form a complex organ: Imagine that a million monkeys are pounding a million typewriters for a million years; will they eventually compose Dante's *Divine Comedy* or a Shakespearian tragedy, or some other great work? Of course, such an event is so improbable that any theory that would necessitate making any such assumption would have to be rejected.

The "monkey analogy" and the objection it illustrates are misleading; they overlook one crucial point: that evolution is a historical process, not simply assembling a body from previously scattered and unrelated parts. The organisms now living on earth are products of at least two billion years of evolutionary development, which was at all times controlled by natural selection. It is wrong to envisage evolution as being like an automobile assembly line which, after the last bolt and the last screw have been placed where they belong, produces an automobile or another complex machine ready to be driven. The automobile is not being used while it moves on the assembly line; our ancestors were alive and therefore were at all times at least tolerably well adapted to their environments, for otherwise they would be extinct and we would not be here. If organic evolution is to be compared with the construction of a machine at all, a more nearly valid comparison would be with the gradual "evolution" of automobiles or airplanes, beginning with the most primitive and going on to the most modern models.

There is a minority of biologists who remain unconvinced by the arguments set forth above. To these biologists, there is something incredible in the Darwinian (or neo-Darwinian) theory that such "blind" and "purposeless" agencies as mutation and natural selection are the sources of the evolution that makes living beings better adapted to their environment. Since the truth or falsity of a scientific theory cannot be settled by majority vote, it is only fair that we should inquire whether any valid alternative to the biological theory of evolution* has been proposed.

Several alternative theories have, in fact, been advanced; they differ rather widely among themselves, but have in common the assumption of so-called orthogenesis or autogenesis. Orthogenesis is evolution following a straight line, or evolution directed by some force residing inside the organism itself. We are invited to believe that the sequence of genetic changes that constitutes evolution is set by the structure of the hereditary materials themselves. The environment and natural selection can only accept or reject these changes. Ultimately, the evolutionary machine was designed and wound up, like a watch, at the beginning of life; all that has happened since is that this machine is gradually unwinding itself in a predeterminate way. Some believers in orthogenesis assume that evolutionary changes are planned and managed by some inscrutable, immaterial, or supernatural force.

Paleontologists, the students of fossils, among whom G. G. Simpson did more than anybody else to evaluate critically the theories of orthogenesis, have shown how completely unacceptable these theories are. If evolution was designed and is managed by a supernatural force, it is managed remarkably badly. Far from following any kind of straight-line progression from simple to complex body structure, from less to more perfect adaptation, or from lower organisms to man, evolution is, rather, like groping

* The theory of evolution by natural selection advanced by Darwin and his immediate followers is correctly referred to as "Darwinism." The name "neo-Darwinism" properly belongs to the theories of Weismann and other authors, which were current early in the present century, but this label is sometimes misapplied also to the modern view, which is better known as the biological, or "synthetic," theory of evolution.

in the dark, which most commonly leads to disaster and
only rarely to success. The "disaster" is, of course, death
and extinction. It is one of the most conspicuous features in
the picture of evolution revealed by paleontology that a
majority of evolutionary lines represented by fossils in the
earth's rocks have eventually become extinct, without
descendants living at present. Emergence of a successful
new group of organisms is a relatively rare occurrence. The
panorama revealed by paleontology suggests a grandiose
trial-and-error operation.

Genetics gives us an idea of how vast this trial-and-error
operation really is. We have seen that the processes of
meiosis and fertilization generate ever-new combinations of
genes (Figure 8 and page 46). The importance of the
recombination and reassortment of genes should not be
underestimated; different combinations of the same genes
are not always mere variations on the same theme, since
gene interactions can produce real novelties. This is best
illustrated by the fact of human individuality—barring
mutation, all the genes I have were present in my parents,
and yet I am a person separate and distinct from them. The
number of different genotypes, genetic endowments, generated in sexually reproducing outbreeding organisms is
truly "astronomical." As shown in the second chapter of
this book, the genotype of every person (excepting identical twins) is just as unique and as novel as that of every
individual mouse, fly, or corn plant.

There are, then, a prodigious number of ever-new genotypes that are constantly being generated by life, and are
being tried out for their fitness to survive and to leave
progeny by natural selection. Natural selection is a process
efficient only in a statistical sense; fitter genotypes are on
the average favored and the genes they contain are multiplied, and the less well-adapted ones discriminated against.
Nevertheless, natural selection brings about a result that, as
the "monkey analogy" suggests, would be utterly improbable without it. The unsteady, erratic, even blundering,

course of the evolutionary histories revealed by the paleon-
tological evidence is, surely, just what is expected on the
basis of this theory. Many evolutionary lines are lost in
blind alleys of adaptation to environments that do not last
long. Extinction is the price paid for the creativity of
evolution.

Is, then, the emergence of man due to the operation of
chance or of an orthogenetic design in evolution? Was
man planned or did he arise by accident? It is necessary to
think about these questions carefully to see how misleading
is the way in which they are so frequently asked. Every
event in nature has an antecedent cause; a chance or accident is an event the causation of which is so complex that
we are unable to predict it. For example, in a game of cards
it is due to chance what hand will be dealt from a well-
shuffled deck, or in a game of dice how the dice will fall;
there would, however, be nothing "chancy" about these
events if we knew in detail every slightest movement of
the person shuffling the cards or throwing the dice. In this
sense, there is nothing accidental about evolution in general or about human evolution in particular. Man's evolution was designed or planned, however, only in the same
sense in which anything and everything that happens anywhere in the whole vast universe was also planned and
determined. On the other hand, evolution is not a matter
of chance, even in the sense in which a game of dice is a
game of chance.

It is reasonable to say that mutation and gene recombination are phenomena involving an element of chance,
but, by the same token, natural selection must be recognized as an anti-chance agency. It not merely screens the
mutants and gene combinations that arise, to preserve the
relatively fit and to eliminate the relatively unfit; it acts as
a regulatory mechanism of the type known as "feedback."
The challenges emanating from the environment are
passed to the genes, and the responses changing the hereditary endowment of the organism create new challenges

which are responded to by new changes. The results do not add up to anything like a straight-line direction of evolution. Evolution is, rather, what among human enterprises is called a creative activity; it produces new and adaptively coherent forms of life, and yet it constantly faces the danger of failure or miscreation, that is, death and extinction.

A question that seemed fanciful even twenty years ago, but which a lot of people are discussing quite seriously nowadays, concerns the possibility of the existence of extraterrestrial life on other planets in our own or in other solar systems. And, further, if such extraterrestrial life does exist, could it be expected to have evolved approximately as life on earth has evolved? Finally, will man, or an organism even roughly resembling man, necessarily arise in evolution enacted on cosmic bodies with environments somewhat similar to the one that prevailed on earth when terrestrial evolution was going on? These questions may become answerable by direct observation in a future not too distant; as of today, I am inclined to wager that man is quite unique in the cosmos. The reason for my skepticism (if this *is* skepticism!) is precisely that evolution is a creative process, and not straight-line orthogenesis. Even granting that some kind of extraterrestrial life exists, and, further, that the environments on some planet are more or less similar to terrestrial ones, the adaptations to the same environments may be achieved in many different ways. It would be quite an extraordinary coincidence if the evolutionary histories happened to be nearly identical in two, or in more than two, different worlds.

One recent author who described evolution as "orthogenesis" was Teilhard de Chardin, whose interesting and original thinking was based on his knowledge of paleontology, as well as of philosophy and theology. My reading of his fascinating book *The Phenomenon of Man,* and of some other of his writings, convinces me that he used the word "orthogenesis" not in the technical biological, but in a philosophical and mystical, sense. He argues that the evolution of the living world so far has been on the whole progressive, an affirmation to which almost nobody will take exception. The manifestation of progress, or at least one of its manifestations, is the rise of consciousness. The highest development of this progressive trend is man. This reading of the evolutionary past and present he then extrapolates to the future. This future lies in "megasynthesis," in an ultimate convergence of all separate consciousnesses in a harmonious union of the "Point Omega," which is a mystical symbol used for God. He asks a rhetorical question: "In the direction of thought, could the universe terminate with anything less than the measureless—any more than it could in the direction of time and space?" His answer is clearly that it could not. His mystical "orthogenesis" need not be incompatible with modern biological theory.

Natural Selection and the Struggle for Life

Let us return to the less-speculative topic of how natural selection works here on earth. Darwin reasoned that all organisms produce more progeny than can survive. Even the slowest-reproducing forms, such as man and the elephant, would, if all their progeny survived, eventually exhaust their food supply or fill all the space in which they can live. This does not happen in reality, because in any species most of the progeny are eliminated by death before they reach maturity. Which individuals survive and which are eliminated is not, however, a matter of chance alone. All living species are variable; some variants are stronger, better adapted to their environment, and they survive more frequently than the less-fit variants. The fitness is in part genetically conditioned. Succeeding generations are descended to a greater extent from the better-adapted variants than from the less-well-adapted ones, and their average level of adaptedness to the environment is therefore higher.

In short, natural selection is due to the survival of the fittest in the struggle for life. This terse formula is partly metaphorical, as any reasonably attentive reading of Darwin's works will clearly show. The "struggle" is not necessarily contention, strife, war, or combat. Desert plants struggle against aridity by reducing leaves to spines, by developing protective devices against water loss, or by growing, flowering, and maturing seeds rapidly during the short rainy season. These plants do not struggle with each other by jabbing their spines into other plants. Animals struggle against cold by seeking warmer places, by developing warm fur, or by other physiological adaptations to withstand cold; they do not struggle by forcing each other to freeze. The survival of the "fittest" does not mean that just one fittest variant survives and the rest die; what is fit to survive survives.

In vain did some naturalists point out that success in the struggle for existence is at least as often achieved among animals by co-operation and mutual help as by competition and combat. Many people preferred to take Darwin's metaphors quite literally. The ideas that struggle without quarter or mercy is a universal law of Nature and that harsh and ruthless competition results in biological progress and improvement were grasped as ready justifications of power politics, conquest, exploitation of the weak by the strong, child labor, and even of laissez-faire economics. Racism, which reached its ugliest forms in Hitler's Germany, but which is very much alive in South Africa and in many places closer to home, also tries to appear decent and "scientific" in a Darwinian garb.

Such attempts to misuse the theory of evolution as an excuse for man's inhumanity to man are evidently a travesty of science. Not all is sweetness and light in biological nature; the lion stalks an unwary antelope, the larva of a parasitic wasp consumes slowly the innards of a caterpillar, in tropical forests a plant, the strangling fig, strangulates and kills the tree on which it lives. It does not follow that humans must stalk, strangulate, and devour each other. Natural selection could, theoretically, occur even if the entire progeny produced in a population survived, provided that the number of children born per couple varied depending on the genetic qualities of the parents. Something of this sort may well be approached in some insects which produce several generations per year; their populations expand rapidly during favorable seasons, only to be decimated more or less randomly during the winter or another unfavorable season. While the population expands, the more fecund genotypes will increase in frequency relative to other genetic endowments.

The development of genetics has made possible a better understanding of natural selection. The selectively fit, or, if you will, the fittest, is not necessarily a fellow with big muscles, or a lusty fighter, or a conqueror of all his competitors. He is, rather, a paterfamilias who has raised a large number of children who in turn become patresfamilias. Of course, a genotype that produces a disease that causes death in childhood has a zero fitness, because its carriers have no progeny. And yet, good health, vigor, and vitality contribute to Darwinian fitness only to the extent that they result in large progenies. The fitness of a genotype is defined and measured by its contribution to the gene pool of the succeeding generation relative to the contribution of other genotypes. Darwinian fitness is reproductive fitness.

Varieties of Natural Selection

An alternative to the classical description of natural selection as the survival of the fittest in the struggle for life may sound something like this: The perpetuation of the fit in the struggle for reproduction. These alternatives are really not as different as they seem to be. Survival and reproduction are evidently complementary; a species or a population must survive in order to reproduce, and they must reproduce in order to survive in the next generation. The modern emphasis on reproductive success as a measure of the Darwinian fitness of a hereditary endowment raises, nevertheless, a very real problem: If natural selection in man maintains and accentuates chiefly the reproductive powers of human populations, will this be beneficial for the maintenance or improvement of human cultural potentialities? Especially in view of the dangers of an uncontrolled population explosion now bedeviling mankind, reproductive proficiency is surely not the only quality that we admire in our fellow men.

To secure an understanding of this problem we must traverse again some of the ground considered on pages 126-133, from a different point of view. There are several kinds of natural selection, of which the simplest is the normalizing selection. We have seen that the dominant gene for achondroplastic dwarfism arises by mutation in about four out of 100,000 sex cells produced by normal persons. Although the health of dwarfs, when they grow up, is not much below normal, many of them remain unmarried and have no children. Mørch found that in Denmark the dwarfs produce about twenty children for every hundred born to their nondwarf siblings. This means that about 80 per cent of the dwarf genes are eliminated from the population in every generation by natural selection.

Juvenile amaurotic idiocy causes a severe degeneration of nerve cells in the brain, which leads to the death of afflicted infants, usually before the age of three. The disease is owing to a recessive mutant in double dose. The parents of infants with this disease are carriers of a single dose of the same mutant gene, but the health of such carriers seems to suffer no impairment. Persons who are carriers of this and other harmful recessive genes are much more numerous in human populations than persons suffering from the effects of such genes in double dose. Achondroplastic dwarfism and juvenile amaurotic idiocy are, of course, only examples of harmful genes that are introduced in populations by the mutation process and are kept under control by normalizing natural selection. As shown in the foregoing chapter, human as well as animal and plant populations always carry genetic loads, that is, genes for various hereditary diseases, defects, and weaknesses.

The gene for sickle-cell anemia is maintained in populations that live in malarial countries by the balancing form of natural selection. As stated previously, the heterozygous carriers of this gene not only enjoy generally good health, but are, in addition, rather more resistant to certain kinds of malarial fevers than are "normal" noncarriers. Although persons who inherit this gene from both parents (homozygotes) die of fatal anemia, the heterozygous carriers may be said to show a hybrid vigor, or heterosis, in malaria-ridden environments. As long as the population is exposed to malaria, natural selection will keep this gene "balanced" in the population. The ill-adapted homozygotes are a part of the balanced genetic load of the population. The interesting property of the balanced load is that it is maintained not by recurrent mutation, as is the mutational load, but by natural selection itself.

The normalizing and the balancing forms of natural selection are, in their essence, conservative forces. They serve to weed out, as far as possible, the harmful genes that the process of mutation constantly spawns, and to buffer the genetic endowment of the species against environmental changes that are only temporary and passing. Directional natural selection brings innovation. Genes that were once upon a time useful when the species lived in a certain environment may become inferior as the environment changes. Directional selection replaces the old genes with new ones better suited for new conditions. It was a long-continued directional selection that gradually transformed the genetic endowment of our animal ancestor, and built the genetic basis on which human culture arose and developed. It favored the ability to make and to use tools, to communicate by means of a symbolic language, to co-operate with one's neighbors in common undertakings, and a host of other human traits and abilities. The selection favored these traits and abilities for one simple reason—their possession conferred on their carriers advantages that enabled them to transmit their genes to the succeeding generations more often than the noncarriers did.

Does natural selection continue to operate in modern mankind? Some scientists and popular writers have contended that it does not. Warnings and prophesies of dire calamities have been issued on this basis—mankind is headed for biological decadence and even extinction. Indeed, suspension of natural selection would be a serious matter. In the long run it would be disastrous, if natural selection were not replaced by some other agency, such as an artificial selection, capable of performing some of the same functions as did natural selection. Here, then, is a problem of utmost importance, surely one of the most serious ones that mankind has to face. It must be examined carefully, with a firm resolve to avoid hasty conclusions not warranted by the evidence available.

Are Culture and Natural Selection Compatible?

It is simply not true that natural selection has ceased to operate in the human species. To make this clear, let us ask ourselves how one could possibly do away with natural selection, if that were desirable. One theoretically possible, but not practically realizable, method would be to have every pair of parents produce the same number of children, all these children without exception to survive, to marry, and again to produce the same number of progeny. Another, and equally fantastic, way to abolish natural selection would be to have the number of children that a couple may produce determined by drawing lots, so that the fertility of the parents would in no way depend on their genes, to have all children survive to maturity, and then either all to marry, or some, chosen by lot, to remain unmarried. Surely nothing like this ever happened anywhere in recorded history.

Genes for amaurotic idiocy are still being eliminated by death, and those for achondroplasia by failure of some dwarfs to find mates. The problem is not whether natural selection still operates, for surely it does. In a way, the problem is a more serious one—whether or not the selection is now doing what we, men, consider good and desirable. Natural selection certainly does not work at present as it did in the man of the Stone Age or in precivilized societies. This is both inevitable and beneficial. Civilized environments present challenges utterly different from those of the environments of the past, and we wish to be fit to live in our present environments, not in those of the Middle Ages or of the Stone Age.

It is certainly true that normalizing selection has become relaxed in human populations with respect to some undesirable mutant genes. In a foregoing chapter (pages 68-72) we have considered examples of hereditary diseases that can be "cured" by medical or surgical treatment. An infant with retinoblastoma may have his life saved by surgical removal of the afflicted eye; galactosemia is not fatal if the galactose is removed from the diet; acrodermatitis enteropatica is cured by a special drug; diabetes mellitus by insulin; myopia by wearing properly made glasses. In short, medicine, hygiene, and civilized conditions save many lives that would otherwise be cut short. This situation is here to stay, or to develop further when the medical sciences learn to control many now "incurable" genetically conditioned defects. Nobody in his right mind would want it to be otherwise.

Unless persons who know that they are carriers of genetic defects refrain from having children, they pass the defective genes to their progenies. The lives saved will thus engender new lives which will stand in need of being saved in the generations to come. The numbers of genetically more or less gravely incapacitated persons will then grow from generation to generation. This is so because the mutation process will continue to add defective genes at the same rate it always did, or even at still higher rates if the mutagenic radiations and other mutagens are not controlled. It is a depressing thought that we are helping the ailing, the lame, and the deformed only to make our descendants more ailing, more lame, and more deformed. Here, then, is a dilemma—if we enable the weak and the deformed to live and to propagate their kind, we face the prospect of a genetic twilight; but if we let them die or suffer when we can save or help them, we face the certainty of a moral twilight.

There is no easy escape from this dilemma. The problem of controlling and guiding human evolution has no single or simple solution. But neither is it hopelessly insoluble. Each genetic condition will have to be considered on its own merits, since it is certain that the measures taken for different conditions will not be the same. A few examples will make clear why this is so. The surgical treatment of retinoblastoma involves removal of the afflicted eyes, which leaves the person blind. Having retinoblastoma more widespread than it is, no doubt, is undesirable. Education that would make people familiar with elementary genetics and biology may be a real help here; it is perhaps not excessively optimistic to hope that a person who is blind because of retinoblastoma, and who knows that his progeny is liable to inherit his defect, may draw the proper conclusion from this knowledge and refrain from having children. Genetic counseling, when individual persons or couples seek and receive advice from competent physicians or specialists in human genetics, can also play an important role. Apart from being informed about the risks and the odds of the appearance of undesirable genetic traits in the progeny, people often stand in need of psychological support. They must be made to realize that being carriers of undesirable genes need not lead to feelings of guilt or of shame. Genetic counseling in so-called heredity clinics is becoming more and more widespread in civilized countries.

To be sure, different persons will not always reach the same decision on the basis of the same facts. Is it, for example, such hard luck to be an achondroplastic dwarf that the risk of having an achondroplastic child must always be avoided? And what about diabetes mellitus, a condition already so widespread, especially if the manifestations of this genetic defect can be reasonably well kept under control by insulin treatment? Finally, with respect to myopia, only fanatics would urge that all myopics should be sterilized or otherwise prevented from having children. Our society can probably stand having myopia become somewhat more widespread than it is now; the remedy is not sterilization, but provisions for more pairs of glasses to be manufactured.

The relaxation of normalizing natural selection with respect to some traits has been so much written and talked about that one should be reminded that there is also the reverse side of this coin. With respect to other traits, normalizing selection is not less, but more rigid in civilized than in primitive man. A dominant gene, which is not rare in the white population of South Africa, produces so-called porphyria, a condition that used to have little effect on the survival or fertility of its carriers. The porphyrics are, however, highly sensitive to the effects of barbiturates, and may be paralyzed and die as a result of medical treatments beneficial to nonporphyrics. Another gene, causing a deficiency of a certain enzyme in the blood (glucose-6-phosphate dehydrogenase, abbreviated G6PD), is rather widespread in some populations living in malarial countries. There is good reason to suppose that it was useful, because it conferred some resistance to malaria. Certain drugs, such as primaquine and sulfonamides, induce, however, a dangerous anemia in persons with this gene.

These persons also suffer a serious illness, called favism, after a meal of fresh fava beans, which are eaten by persons free of this gene without any unpleasant consequences. Favism has long been known, but its dependence on the gene for the enzyme deficiency has been discovered only recently.

Considering mankind as a whole, the above genetic traits are not very common and therefore not very important. It may be otherwise with genes that confer resistance to, or predispose toward, nervous breakdown and nervous disorders. It is at least possible that the selection for such resistance has become more rigorous in technologically advanced societies than it was under more primitive, or, if you wish, more "natural" conditions. The life of Stone Age man, or, for that matter, of a peasant tilling the soil, was not free of stresses and worries. These stresses were, however, of kinds different from those to which we are exposed, and it is at least possible that the genes that confer resistance to them are not the same.

I do not wish to be understood as maintaining that the genetic future of mankind is safe and need not cause any concern. Above all, it should be realized that not enough is known about this tremendous problem. Genetics in general, and genetics of man in particular, are in urgent need of more research. For if natural selection does not function as man wishes that it would, then remedial measures must be taken. Natural selection must be replaced by eugenical artificial selection. This idea constitutes the sound core of eugenics, the applied science of human betterment.

Negative and positive eugenics can be distinguished. The former seeks methods to discourage the spread of undesirable genes, and the latter to encourage the spread of desirable ones. Unfortunately, the idea of eugenics suffered grievous harm at the hands of its overenthusiastic supporters. Especially between 1900 and 1930, some partisans of eugenics were making rash promises, such as that all social ills would disappear within a few generations if their pet programs were to be adopted. Eugenics was compromised even more badly when for a period of about a third of a century it was captured by people who wanted it to become a pseudo-scientific basis of a reactionary political philosophy. It is to be hoped that a more scientific eugenics will overcome this reputation.

The eugenical programs advanced in recent years by some eminent scientists may also be questioned. It has been proposed, for example, that the seminal fluid of superior men be collected and preserved in a frozen condition, so that it can be used, possibly for many years to come, for artificial insemination of women who will supposedly be happy to become mothers of children of superior sires. The proposal, in fact, goes far beyond this "modest" beginning. Techniques should be developed to obtain not only superior spermatozoa of males, but also egg cells of superior females. The finest egg cells will be combined with the choicest spermatozoa; the fertilized eggs will then be implanted to develop in the uteri of women who are not good enough to propagate their own genes, but nevertheless qualified to nurture the superior fetuses and the resulting infants and children. Further, techniques are to be invented to obtain fetuses from a tissue culture of body cells of superior individuals; this would guarantee the finest genetic endowment in the progeny.

Such programs remind one of the *Brave New World* utopia devised by Aldous Huxley as a warning against treating human beings as though they were mere automata. The objection against these programs is not only that they attempt to flout some of the emotions dearest to human beings. They also presume that we know far more than we actually do about what kinds of genetic endowments would be best for man to have, not only at present, but also in the remote future. It can show no lack of respect for the greatness of men like Darwin, Galileo, and Beethoven, to name only a few, to say that a world with many millions of Darwins, Galileos, or Beethovens may not be the best possible world.

Outlook for the Future

It is an error to think that the progress of mankind would be safe and irresistible if only natural selection were permitted to operate unobstructed by civilization. Natural selection does not guarantee even the survival of the species, let alone its improvement. Dinosaurs became extinct despite their evolution having been piloted by natural selection quite unhampered by culture. Natural selection is automatic, mechanical, blind. It brings about genetic changes that often, though not always, appear to be purposeful, furthering the survival and opposing the extinction of the species. And yet, natural selection has no purpose. Only man can have purposes.

Man, if he so chooses, may introduce his purposes into his evolution. Man's biological predicament is not that natural selection has ceased to act; it is that the selection may not be doing what we wish it to do. Man is the sole product of evolution who has achieved the knowledge that he came into this universe out of animality by means of evolution. He may choose to direct his evolution toward the attainment of the purposes he regards as good, or which he believes to represent the will of the Creator.

The crux of the matter is evidently what purposes, aims, or goals we should choose to strive for. Let us not delude ourselves with easy answers. One such answer is that a superior knowledge of human biology would make it unmistakable which plan is the best and should be followed. Another is that biological evolution has itself implanted in man ethical ideas and inclinations favorable for this evolution's continued progress. Now, I would be among the last to doubt that biology sheds some light on human nature; but for planning even the biological evolution of mankind, let alone its cultural evolution, biology is palpably insufficient.

Some biologists, among whom Julian Huxley is probably the most famous modern representative, thought that man's discrimination between good and evil is a product of biological evolution. Our ethics are built by past natural selection as a part of our biological nature. This is too much to claim for evolution. As C. H. Waddington neatly puts it, what evolution has done is to make us "ethicizing beings" and "authority acceptors," especially in childhood. Just as our genes determine our ability to speak but not what we shall say, so the ethical principles we accept come not from our biological, but from our cultural inheritance. Man's biological evolution has produced an organic basis for his cultural evolution. It is in order to serve as the foundation for man's cultural advancement that man's biological nature must be not only maintained but, if possible, improved and ennobled. In planning human evolution, including biological evolution, biology must be guided by man's spiritual and cultural heritage. Religion, philosophy, art, man's entire accumulated wisdom and experience are here indispensable.

Human evolution has forced mankind to a crossroad from which there is no turning back and no escape. Our animal past is irretrievably lost—we could not go back to it even if we wished to. The choice is between a twilight, cultural as well as biological, or a progressive adaptation of man's genes to his culture, and of man's culture to his genes. I am optimistic enough to hope that the right choices will be achieved before it is too late. Some people call our age the Age of Anxiety, and this puts optimism in need of justification. I am an optimist because I know that mankind, the living world, and the whole universe have evolved and are evolving. Look into yourself and look at the world around you. Everywhere there is a tremendous amount of ugliness as well as of beauty, much that is good and admirable and a lot that is evil and horrible. My point is that the knowledge that we are evolving bestows hope. Whether one feels that beauty and good or that ugliness and evil predominate in the world, one knows that this world was not created all at once, fixed and unchangeable forever. Creation is not an event, but a process, not complete but continuing. Progress and betterment are by no means guaranteed or vouchsafed in evolution. However, man may strive to bring them about, and this striving is what gives meaning and dignity to human life, individually and collectively. So, let me repeat, evolution bestows hope.

Suggestions for Further Reading

As stated in the Preface, no attempt has been made in this book to survey the field of genetics. Nor, for that matter, could one possibly attempt, within the limits of the size and of the character of this book, to discuss in any detail the modern theories of biological evolution, or the fascinating problem of the origin of man from prehuman ancestors, or the much-discussed dangers of genetic damage by radiation, or the perspectives and potentialities of eugenics. The following are references to publications to which the reader looking for further information may turn.

Books describing fundamentals of genetics are at present quite numerous. For orientation in general genetics one may suggest:

Herskowitz, I. H. *Genetics.* Little, Brown, Boston, 1962.
Muntzing, A. *Genetic Research.* LTs Forlag, Stockholm, 1961.
Sinnott, E. W., L. C. Dunn, and Th. Dobzhansky. *Principles of Genetics.* 5th Edition. McGraw-Hill, New York, 1958.

A splendid book on general genetics, with a special emphasis on human genetics is:

Stern, C. *Principles of Human Genetics.* 2nd Edition. Freeman, San Francisco, 1960.

Books dealing more specifically with human genetics are, among others:

Clarke, C. A. *Genetics for the Clinician*. Davis, Philadelphia, 1962.

Frazer-Roberts, J. A. *An Introduction to Medical Genetics*. Oxford University Press, London, 1963.

Lenz, W. *Medical Genetics*. University of Chicago Press, Chicago, 1963.

Neel, J. V., and W. J. Schull. *Human Heredity*. University of Chicago Press, Chicago, 1954.

Penrose, L. S. *Outline of Human Genetics*. J. Wiley, New York, 1963.

Reed, S. C. *Counseling in Medical Genetics*. 2nd Edition. Saunders, Philadelphia, 1963.

Vogel, F. *Lehrbuch der Allgemeinen Humangenetik*. Springer, Berlin, 1961.

For accounts of molecular genetics (a field progressing so rapidly that books dealing with this subject become out of date very quickly), see the books addressed to a general reader:

Asimov, I. *The Genetic Code*. New American Library, New York, 1962.

Borek, E. *The Atoms Within Us*. Columbia University Press, New York, 1961.

More advanced sources are, among many others:

Anfinsen, Ch. B. *The Molecular Basis of Evolution*. J. Wiley, New York, 1959.

Ingram, V. M. *Hemoglobin and Its Abnormalities*. Ch. Thomas, Springfield, 1961.

Ingram, V. M. *The Hemoglobins in Genetics and Evolution*. Columbia University Press, New York, 1963.

Sager, R., and F. J. Ryan. *Cell Heredity*. J. Wiley, New York, 1961.

For genetic studies on behavior and the nature-nurture problem see:

Fuller, J. L., and W. R. Thompson. *Behavior Genetics*. J. Wiley, New York, 1960.

Kallmann, F. J. *Heredity in Health and Mental Disorder*. Norton, New York, 1953.

Roe, A., and G. G. Simpson. *Behavior and Evolution*. Yale University Press, New Haven, 1958.

Shields, J. *Monozygotic Twins Brought Up Apart and Brought Up Together*. Oxford University Press, London, 1962.

Quantitative aspects of population genetics that are basic for understanding the problems of evolutionary dynamics, and particularly the dangers of genetic damage by radiation in human populations, are dealt with in:

Lerner, I. M. *The Genetic Basis of Selection*. J. Wiley, New York, 1958.

Li, C. C. *Population Genetics*. University of Chicago Press, Chicago, 1955.

Li, C. C. *Human Genetics*. McGraw-Hill, New York, 1961.

National Academy of Sciences. *The Biological Effects of Atomic Radiation*. Summary Reports, Washington, 1960. (In this Report, see particularly the statement by Sewall Wright, pages 18-24.)

Rasmuson, M. *Genetics on the Population Level*. Svenska Bokforlaget, Stockholm, 1961.

Spiess, E. B. (Editor). *Papers on Animal Population Genetics*. Little, Brown, Boston, 1962. (This is an anthology of many articles in the field of population genetics, some of them rather inaccessible in the original.)

United Nations. *Report of Scientific Committee on the Effects of Atomic Radiations*. United Nations, New York, 1962.

Wallace, B., and Th. Dobzhansky. *Radiations, Genes, and Man*. Henry Holt, New York, 1959. (There is an abbreviated edition, adapted by F. N. Paparello. Holt, Rinehart, & Winston, New York, 1963.)

The fundamentals of the modern biological theory of evolution, and some of the more general humanistic and philosophical implications of this theory, have in recent years been presented by:

Carson, H. L. *Heredity and Human Life*. Columbia University Press, New York, 1963.

Dobzhansky, Th. *Evolution, Genetics, and Man.* J. Wiley, New York, 1955. (Paperback edition, J. Wiley, 1963.)

Dobzhansky, Th. *The Biological Basis of Human Freedom.* Columbia University Press, New York, 1956. (Paperback edition, Columbia University Press, 1960.)

Ehrlich, P. R., and R. W. Holm. *The Process of Evolution.* McGraw-Hill, New York, 1963.

Simpson, G. G. *The Meaning of Evolution.* Yale University Press, New Haven, 1949. (Paperback edition, Yale University Press, 1962.)

Simpson, G. G. *This View of Life: The World of an Evolutionist.* Harcourt, Brace & World, New York, 1964.

The classical works of Darwin, particularly *On the Origin of Species* and *The Descent of Man* are not only still readable, but, in fact, indispensable to anybody who wishes to understand the essence and the background of the evolution theory. Darwin's works are available in many editions. More technical works, written by authors who approached the subject from the points of view of different biological disciplines, and yet more or less converged on a single over-all theory, are, among others, the following:

Dobzhansky, Th. *Genetics and the Origin of Species.* 3rd Edition. Columbia University Press, New York, 1951. (Paperback edition, Columbia University Press, 1964).

Grant, V. *The Origin of Adaptations.* Columbia University Press, New York, 1963.

Grant, V. *The Architecture of the Germplasm.* J. Wiley, New York, 1964.

Ford, E. B. *Ecological Genetics.* Methuen and John Wiley, London and New York, 1964.

Huxley, J. S. *Evolution, the Modern Synthesis.* Harper, New York, 1942.

Mayr, E. *Animal Species and Evolution.* Harvard University Press, Cambridge, 1963.

Rensch, B. *Evolution Above the Species Level.* Columbia University Press, New York, 1960.

Schmalhausen, I. I. *Factors of Evolution.* Blakiston, Philadelphia, 1949.

Simpson, G. G. *The Major Features of Evolution*. Columbia University Press, New York, 1953.

Simpson, G. G. *Principles of Animal Taxonomy*. Columbia University Press, New York, 1961.

Stebbins, G. L. *Variation and Evolution in Plants*. Columbia University Press, New York, 1950.

Tax, S. (Editor). *Evolution After Darwin*. 3 volumes. University of Chicago Press, Chicago, 1960. (This is a collection of papers by many authors, delivered on the occasion of the celebration of the Darwin Centennial at the University of Chicago; in the aggregate, they give a panorama of the present state of the theory of evolution.)

Books dealing entirely or largely with the evolution of mankind are numerous. The following ones may be recommended for an orientation in the diversity of opinions existing in this important, fascinating, but perennially controversial field:

Carrington, R. *A Million Years of Man*. World Publishers, Cleveland and New York, 1963.

Clark, W. C. Le Gros. *The Fossil Evidence for Human Evolution*. Chicago University Press, Chicago, 1955.

Coon, C. S. *The Origin of Races*. Knopf, New York, 1962.

Dobzhansky, Th. *Mankind Evolving*. Yale University Press, New Haven, 1962.

Gardner, J. W. *Excellence*. Harper, New York, 1961.

Garn, S. M. *Human Races*. Ch. Thomas, Springfield, 1961.

Haller, M. H. *Eugenics*. Rutgers University Press, New Brunswick, 1963.

Howells, W. W. *Mankind in the Making*. Doubleday, Garden City, 1959.

Howells, W. W. (Editor). *Ideas on Human Evolution. Selected Essays*. Harvard University Press, Cambridge, 1962.

Hulse, F. S. *The Human Species*. Random House, New York, 1963.

Montagu, Ashley M. F. *An Introduction to Physical Anthropology*. 3rd Edition. Ch. Thomas, Springfield, 1960.

Mourant, A. E. *The Distribution of the Human Blood Groups*. Blackwell, Oxford, 1954.

Osborn, F. *Preface to Eugenics*. Rev. Edition, Harper, New York, 1951.

United Nations. *Demographic Yearbook 1962*. United Nations, New York, 1962.

Washburn, S. L. (Editor). *Social Life of Early Man*. Wenner Gren Foundation, New York, 1961.

Washburn, S. L. (Editor). *Classification and Human Evolution*. Wenner Gren Foundation, New York, 1963.

The works of Pierre Teilhard de Chardin, a Christian mystic and a poet, as well as, or perhaps even more than, a scientist, stand in a class of their own. He has attempted to present a poetic vision of Man and his place in the universe. The idea of evolution is the key part of this vision. The principal work available in English is: *The Phenomenon of Man*. Harper, New York, 1959.

Index